THE
SPIRIT
OF
Tocayo

Ancient Insights for a New Age

THE SPIRIT OF Tocayo

Ancient Insights for a New Age

**Steven R. Gottry &
Richard A. Jacobsen**

Priority Publishing Group, Inc.
Mesa, Arizona

Distributed by:
Macalester Park Publishing Co. Inc.
Shakopee, Minnesota

Editor: Helen Motter
Production Editors: Tami Benson and Sarah Beckman
Cover Design/Page Design: Eric Walljasper

Printed in the United States of America
Printing 10 9 8 7 6 5 4 3 2 1

The authors and publisher have designated that a portion of all
royalties and profits received from the sale of this book will be
donated to the following humanitarian causes:

LIFEWATER

A program that provides fresh-water supplies to impoverished
villages in the Dominican Republic, to save the lives of children
who may otherwise perish as the result of unsanitary conditions.

and:

HABITAT FOR HUMANITY

A widely supported effort to build affordable, low-interest
housing for families who join hands through their own labors to
create better lives for themselves.

Dedication

To our wives, Joy Jacobsen and Karla Gottry,
for their support, encouragement, and love.

Contents

Acknowledgments

We're sure we'll overlook someone who deserves credit, but we're not going to let that stop us from trying to acknowledge all those involved.

First, we'd like to thank Michael Beard, publisher at Macalester Park, for throwing his support behind the project.

Thanks to Eric Walljasper, who designed the cover and handled interior page design and composition; and to our editor, Helen Motter, for her invaluable suggestions and fine-tuning of our manuscript.

And thanks to Eugene H. Peterson for his outstanding and highly readable modern-English translation of the ancient Message, as well as to Jim Hoff for his inspiration and teaching.

We would like to thank Richard Smith, Dick Young, Jack Liemandt, and George and Susan Johnson for their supportive words, and Richard Baltzell for his ongoing encouragement.

Thanks to our children Anna and Nathaniel (Ric's), and Jonathan, Michelle, and Kalla Paige (Steve's), for their hugs and affection. They truly add meaning to our lives! We always want to do the same for them.

And thanks to you, our readers, for the honesty and openness with which many of you will approach our work!

Mysteries and Insights

It is, of course, obvious to anyone who has given it some thought that life is full of mysteries. None of us can know all of the answers to the great and small questions of life. So we learn what we can.

The way we learn is through both insights and experience. Though it has been said that "there's no substitute for experience," it can also be said that there's no substitute for the insights we gain from others.

Insights come from a wide variety of sources: from parents and siblings, from teachers and classmates, from books, newspapers, and magazines, from film and the electronic media.

But as we gather the insights of others into our minds and use them as part of our acquired body of knowledge, we have to apply our best judgment to them. You see, not everything we see and hear can be the truth. And not everything we see and hear can have value — or at least not equal value.

It is our task, as unique individuals, to differentiate among the many messages or insights that come our way. We have to sort these insights into four basic categories: those we believe are true and have merit or meaningful application in our lives; those we believe are true but have no value to us or significant impact on our lives; those we believe are the product of someone's imagination, yet have some meaning to us by virtue of how they shape our attitudes, beliefs, and perceptions; and those we believe are fiction but have no real meaning to us.

Consider this book, for example. Those who believe that it is the product of our imagination — in other words, fiction — and read it simply for its value as fiction will likely gain no greater meaning from it. "It was a good read," we hope they'll say. "It was interesting and I really enjoyed it, but I didn't think about it much after I finished it."

Those who view the story as fiction but try to gain insights into their relationships are likely to benefit more from this book than the casual reader will. They may discover concepts that could revolutionize their lives.

Then there is, we believe, that small group of readers who recognize that the basic story is fictional, yet understand, instinctively, that the experiences the characters share are real and genuine and meaningful. These readers are the ones who will benefit most from *The Spirit of Tocayo*.

THE EXCITING THING IS THAT YOU GET TO DECIDE!

The search — the journey — that unfolds on these pages can be viewed as gentle, contemplative entertainment, or it could possibly provoke a new level of thinking and ultimately lead to a heightened level of living.

We hope you'll identify with some of the hopes, fears, frustrations, and questions faced by the characters in our story. If you do, the journey will be more meaningful to you.

But don't read this book expecting to arrive at some predetermined destination. No two readers will come to the same place in their minds or hearts. All that matters is that you are open to where the journey takes you.

Turn the page then...and begin.

The Flight to Tocayo

"If you walk out now," Connie screamed as she pushed her way past me and ran toward our bedroom, "don't bother to come back! Ever!"

She slammed the door, and I heard the lock click into place. I was glad the kids weren't around — they didn't need to hear any more of this. Our "discussion," after all, had been an ongoing one, with nearly two weeks of mealtime conversation devoted to my most recent travel plans.

I had a dilemma going here. My flight left in barely an hour and a half, and my suitcases were on the other side of that door. Besides, Connie was supposed to be my ride to the airport.

It's not like her to detonate in my face, so I decided it would be possible to reason with her, if only she'd let me.

I knocked. There was nothing but silence. "Please open the door and let me in," I thought but decided to let the actual words wait. She was the one in control. I knocked again and tested the knob to find out if the door was really locked. It was.

Through her quiet sobs I finally heard, "Go away, Jeff."

"Can we talk?" I pleaded.

"No."

"Please. I can't just leave. I need you to understand why. I need your support."

Not knowing what to do or say next, I simply stood there. I looked at my watch. Yup, time was indeed marching on.

It took a few moments, but finally I heard her turn the lock. She opened the door and stood there in smudged makeup, a box of tissues in her hand.

"Go, Jeff. If this is something you really have to do, just get your bags and go."

She must have seen the concern and doubt on my face. I was never good at hiding my emotions.

"Yes, I'll be here when you get back."

I was glad to hear those words and put my arms around her.

She pulled back and looked straight in my eyes. "This had better be it, though, Jeff. This had better be the end of it. You're not going to unlock all those secrets you want to. No one ever has."

She was probably right. But I had to know that for an absolute fact.

"You still driving me to the airport?" I asked as I reached for my suitcases.

"Yes...for the last time."

We were about a mile from the airport exit at Century Boulevard before she spoke again. "What do you think you're going to find at this place that you didn't find in Mexico or Arizona? What's so important that you have to leave your wife and kids for another week?"

"I don't know, Connie. There's just something drawing me to

this place. Maybe it's fate."

"I wish fate would keep you home," she muttered under her breath.

"I wish you could understand my struggles. I feel like there's no meaning to anything. I feel like I'm just a guy with a wife and two kids and a house and a job, and not much more."

"Jeff, there's nothing wrong with being a guy with a wife and kids and a job. Millions of men are doing that and being that right now."

"I know," I responded, "but like the song says, I still haven't found what I'm looking for. I want to feel like I'm a part of a greater world — a greater plan. I'm tired of being insignificant."

She took my hand. It was the most tender thing she'd done in months. "You're not insignificant to us. To me and Amy and Josh. We need you. We want you back."

We drove up to the departure level and found the sign for my airline posted at Terminal Two. I checked my pocket for my ticket. I don't know why, but I always check for my ticket after I get to the airport. I should probably do that while I'm still in my driveway.

When I opened the door to step out on the curb, I felt a tug on my shirt sleeve. I looked back and saw more tears forming in Connie's eyes.

"I love you," she said.

"I love you, too," I said as I leaned over to give her a kiss.

I couldn't help but stand there on the sidewalk and watch until her car had completely left my view. Despite the tensions in our marriage lately, I was going to miss her. I knew it wasn't easy for her. She had been through a lot, and it seemed to me there was little I could ever do to help.

All but a few stragglers had boarded the plane when I arrived at the gate. I got my seat assignment — 37E — smack dab in the middle of the third from the last row. I'd hoped to find something a little better once I got on board, but no such luck. I can't believe they can fill up an MD-11 headed for Minnesota! Mexico City, yes. But Minneapolis? Who goes there anyway?

It's amazing what airlines call meals these days. Stuff that should be warm is cold. Stuff that should be cold is warm. And it all tastes the same — but at least they serve tiny portions.

The movie selection didn't interest me in the least, so I saved the four bucks they wanted for headphones and settled back in my cramped seat for a nap. Except I couldn't sleep. My mind was racing along, thoughts piling on top of each other. Would this be another wasted trip? Were my expectations too high? I knew very little about this place — at least I knew what to expect when I went on my other trips. I had seen pictures. But Tocayo Habitat? Never mind that no one I know and respect has ever been there or that I've never seen a brochure on the place. I was headed there solely on the recommendation of a brief acquaintance, and everything I knew about it was based on his description. Tocayo? It doesn't even *sound* real. Still, I promised myself I would approach the experience with an open mind.

The thought that troubled me most was, would Connie really be there for me when I got back home? This search of mine would ultimately mean nothing if she suddenly wasn't a part of my life. I realized that I haven't always felt that way, but I did at that moment. And that, I decided, is what really mattered.

The Journey Continues

"There are only three requirements here," said our leader, Tim, in a voice so calm and quiet I almost ignored him as my mind wandered on to future matters as yet undetermined. "The first is that you must all eat your meals with the group."

Fair enough, I thought. Hate eating alone anyway. I've done it more than enough on business trips.

"The second is that you must maintain silence except when you are talking to me." Also fair, I thought. After all, one of the reasons I had come here was to reflect on my life — what it meant and, hopefully, what it could mean. People, and family, and phone calls, and the incessant sounds of daily life were what I had deliberately left behind. Conversation — especially small talk — was something I could easily do without for the week I would be here.

"Finally," he added, "you must keep a journal of your thoughts and feelings while you are with us. Write in your journal when we give you something to think about, as well as every time you have a thought, a question, or something you want to discuss with me...or someone else...today or at any time in the tomorrows of your future."

NOT fair, I determined, as Tim's associate, whom I had not yet met, distributed small fabric-bound journals to each of us. I didn't like writing that much to begin with, and I had to do more of it than I wanted to in my job. My discontent with my career had increased in direct proportion to the increase in the number of written reports I had to generate. Some of these reports, as near as I could determine, had no useful purpose and probably weren't ever read in their entirety by my supervisors. (I've actually considered slipping an off-color joke into the middle of one of them, just to find out if my readers were paying attention.)

"If you need a pen, see me after this session," Tim's associate whispered to each of us as he gave us our journals.

"You are here at Tocayo Habitat because you are on a journey," Tim continued. "And you are the only one who can go on that journey — no one else will follow the same path, or arrive at the same place at the same time for the same reasons. You are not on this journey to compete with anyone else, and you do not have to measure your pace on your journey, or compare it to anyone else's pace. That is one of the reasons why you are not permitted to talk among yourselves — to avoid comparison."

I grasped the meaning of Tim's comments, but I still decided to glance around the room to survey and count its occupants. There were twenty-two, not including Tim and his associate. Privately, I wanted to know who they were, what they did, and why they were here. I also wanted to know why the women outnumbered the men. Were they more in touch with their "spiritual selves," or did their employers just provide them with better vacation plans?

"This is Michael," said Tim as he finally acknowledged and

introduced his associate. "He's here to make your stay more comfortable and to handle such matters as scheduling your daily private conferences with me."

I wondered to myself — how could Tim possibly find the time for private daily conferences with twenty-two people? Some of them must not have been as filled with questions as I was, I reasoned.

"Michael will be responsible for giving you your cabin assignments. Pick up your luggage where you placed it at the entrance and note the location of your cabin on the map we'll be giving you shortly. If you leave your map in your cabin and forget how to find it later — an unlikely prospect, I'm sure — there's also a map posted by the north exit of this building. Don't bother to dress up for dinner. We're not very formal here." With that comment, Tim seemed to be finished, and he left without saying goodbye. Odd, I thought.

I couldn't WAIT to see my cabin. I had heard about this place on my trip to Sedona. In fact, it was that trip which resulted in this one. I had an image in my mind, thanks to the description I got from an intense young man I met at Pepe Muldoon's Mexican Restaurant. Four walls. A bed. A simple desk with a chair. An old easy chair. And a bathroom with rust-stained fixtures. Pretty swell, huh? Poverty, but with a primitive touch.

Like everyone else, I got in line to pick up a small packet from Michael. In it was the map to my assigned cabin (a simple, crudely drawn thing that also illustrated the many trails running through the property) and a schedule of mealtimes and seminars. Nothing else, not even a key. "Must not need them out in the woods," I figured. "Must be able to trust everyone else who came here." I noted on the schedule that dinner was at 6:30, a little more than two hours later. Plenty of time to get settled and explore a little.

My cabin wasn't too far from the main building — perhaps three hundred yards. I could see it as I stepped outside, though it was mostly hidden by the dense growth of northern spruce and birch trees, with scattered stalwart oak and maple, that covered virtually every square inch of available land. Judging from the map, some of the other cabins appeared to be quite far away. A few were even pictured as being on the small lake on the property. I was a bit envious — a lake view would have suited me just fine.

The scents of the woods became stronger as I walked up the gentle slope to my cabin, all the while staying on the narrow bark-chip covered trail. "Maybe it'll be bigger when I get inside," I thought to myself as I approached the building, which appeared to be about the size of a walk-in closet.

I unlatched the door and went inside. It wasn't any bigger. I set down my bag in about the only open space available. "Yup, I'm at the right place," I said out loud.

It was "as advertised." A single bed with a wrought-iron headboard painted white. A small desk with metal legs, also painted white. A desk chair I knew would be wretchedly uncomfortable — even before I sat on it. A wash basin with a small mirror above it, but no toilet and no shower. It appeared there would be other group activities in addition to meals.

There was no phone, of course, though I noted on the map that there was a phone in one of the hallways of the main building. A note explained that it was "for emergency purposes only." And no easy chair! The idea must be to relax on the bed. I sat down. It had a serious sag in the middle. Between the chair and the bed, I knew I would make my chiropractor a truly "happy camper" upon my return home. *This* little adventure would require ten appointments, versus my old record of eight following my white-water rafting expedition in Colorado last summer with my son. (Who, at nine years of age, didn't seem to experience any adverse effects and wants to go again. Crazy kid.)

I peered out the small window above the desk and was pleasantly surprised by what I saw. Though it was at some distance, I had a view of the lake. Lakes and rivers and streams and oceans have always quieted my restlessness. My first experience with water was at about five years of age when my grandfather took me fishing in a little boat at a resort in northern Michigan. I never got into the fishing — I still have no interest in it — but I sure enjoyed the water and remember to this day the peacefulness of it. (To say that I was a hyperactive child would be a serious understatement. Peacefulness has been a rare and elusive feeling for me all of my life.)

Even as an adult, I'm overwhelmed by the restless feeling that I should be doing something productive every moment of every day. Yet I can calm myself by getting near the water. Any water. That's probably why I insisted that any house we lived in had to have a pool, and why Connie and I had a hot tub installed just outside the door of our bedroom that exits onto the patio.

I glanced at my watch. Not much time had passed — dinner was still nearly two hours away. I was faced with a dilemma. Should I take a nap? Read a book? Write in the stupid journal, or go for a walk? Writing in the journal came in last. The clear winner was going for a walk. Why not get some fresh air and see the lake up close?

I stepped outside, walked around the cabin, and chose a

narrow path that I believed would lead to the lake without passing directly by the other cabins.

As I walked — and drank in the silence — I was reminded of some thoughts in one of the books I had most recently read, *The Celestine Prophecy*. There are more than a few profound truths in that little book. I discovered that, as I shut everything else out, I became more keenly aware of all the wonders of the setting. The true glory of nature flooded all of my senses. I could hear, see, smell, and touch all of the beauty that surrounded me. (I could probably have tasted it, too, but I wasn't sure of what was poisonous and what wasn't!)

Listening to the sound of my feet treading on the path was a unique new experience for me. How many of us, when we walk in the city, are aware of the sounds of our steps? I never was. Among other things, there's too much background noise. Yet now, as I listened to the sound of crunching branches under my feet, I became acutely aware of the cycle of life. Birth, growth, maturity, death. But the dead branches and leaves crushed by my Nikes were contributing to a new generation of living organisms — a generation that was perhaps hundreds or thousands of years in the future. Life from death. What a thought!

As I walked, my arms brushed against the foliage, and I became aware of the contact between nature and humanity. Instead of simply walking past trees and ferns and moss and wild flowers, I looked at them. I discovered they're different when viewed from the front or back, from above or from underneath, in the bright sunlight or in the shade. As I passed by the branch of a particular tree, I studied it. The light played upon it, and I could see its many subtle colors and facets.

It seemed to me that if nature reveals anything, it's that you have to keep moving in life to see and experience the many dimensions of all the things there are to enjoy. You can't stand still.

I imagine that most people who are in tune with nature have sensed these same things and would find nothing unique about what I was experiencing. But for me, living in the "fast lane" of the city, it was something fresh and new. And it was very exciting!

I kept looking for the glow, or "aura," that is supposed to surround living things. Many people believe this glow is energy, but I couldn't see it. My visual sense must have been out of tune. Still, I could feel it. The plants and trees share something important with us. Life. In our own distinct ways, we breathe, we grow, and we pass life on to future generations.

I reached the shoreline and walked out on the narrow dock that extended about thirty or forty feet into the water. There were no boats tied to the dock, and none in sight, so I wondered why they bothered to have a dock in the first place.

There was little wind, and the water was quite calm and clear. I could see the small, smooth pebbles on the bottom. At that moment, a half dozen or more ducks swam by. They moved silently, yet they disturbed the water and left a rippling wake behind them. As stupid as it sounds, I wondered what it would be like to be a duck. I almost felt "in tune" with them, as if there were not all that much that separated us. Then I remembered hunters with 12-gauge shotguns. Ducks must *always* live life on the edge.

My trivial thoughts were interrupted by the ringing of a bell. More like a chime, actually. I knew that meant dinner. I was now amazed at how quickly time had passed. Time, as everyone knows, is relative. If you're bored or have nothing to do, it crawls by. But if you have things to think about, discover, or accomplish, it races

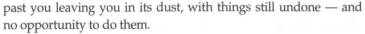

past you leaving you in its dust, with things still undone — and no opportunity to do them.

The other "guests" at Tocayo seemed to magically appear from just about anywhere and everywhere as we made our way toward the main building. This rustic facility, called simply "the lodge," was clad in rough-sawn cedar boards and seemed to be built to accommodate all of the activities of our retreat except sleeping, writing, and walking in nature. There were five rooms open to us. One was the meeting hall where we congregated upon our arrival. The second, third, and fourth, I was to discover later, were Tim's conference office, a library, and a small room designated for meditation and reflection. The latter room could only be used by one person at a time, and there was a sign-up sheet outside the door. The fifth room was the dining room. Naturally, I assumed that the facility included a kitchen and some sort of administrative offices, but all of that was of no consequence. I was hungry.

At the entrance to the dining room, I was told by Michael that there were no assigned places, and I could sit wherever I wanted. He told me, though, that the seat I chose would be mine for my entire stay.

I glanced around the room, looking for an "interesting" table to join. Then I thought, "If I can't talk to anyone — requirement number two — who cares if they look interesting? I'll never know anyway."

All of the tables accommodated six people. I spotted one that had drawn four women and one man. "Can't leave that poor sucker on his own," I jokingly thought to myself, so I joined them.

From the moment I sat down, nothing but surprises unfolded. The first one was that Tim told us we could talk to each other at dinner tonight and also at our final dinner a week from tonight. "So much for silence. Geez, now I gotta talk to all these women!"

The second surprise was that Tim led us all in something that sounded vaguely like "grace." I'd grown up with all that "Bless this food to the use of our bodies" garbage and wasn't at all in the mood for it here. Although, I have to admit, Tim gave it a new twist. He beseeched the "God-Presence" to strengthen us for the journey ahead. I didn't know who the "God-Presence" was, and I was quite sure I didn't *want* to know, but the idea of getting strength for the journey ahead appealed to me. Somehow, I knew this place was going to be a bear.

The third surprise was kind of minor, but it's still worth mentioning. They put on a tape or a CD or something of prerecorded music. They said they were going to play music during every meal. I made a mental note on the music. A guy named Bill Miller playing Native American flute music (I'm serious; this is for real) and a guitarist named John Michael Talbot playing contemplative/meditative music. Someone at my table — Bonnie-Something-or-Other — said the Talbot guy's a monk who used to be in a rock band. Well, there's a switch for you.

The dinner was pretty good, though no wine. Seems to me a good pasta dish needs — no, *deserves* — a good Italian wine alongside it. This *was* a good pasta dish, too. All natural ingredients. Low fat. No meat. No kiddin'. It was accompanied by a salad, but the Italian dressing was pretty bland. I like my spices. (Okay, I promise, no more talk about food. You don't care what I ate anyway.)

I have to admit, I rather liked the Bill Miller and John Michael Talbot music. With kids in the house, I've had as much of Madonna as I can stand. These quiet flute and guitar compositions really did calm me. Too bad they don't play this kind of music on the radio.

The thought occurred to me that there would be no point in getting to know the other people at my table, since I wouldn't talk to them for a week, and after that, I'd probably never see them again.

But, hey, this was an entire dinner in my life — I may as well make it matter for something.

The woman to my immediate left was a congresswoman from a New England state. (I won't mention her by name in case she doesn't get re-elected.) I probably shouldn't have let that fact affect me, but suddenly I felt insignificant. Although, what does it take to get elected to Congress? A smooth line — promise everyone everything — and money. Probably more money than I'll ever see.

Next to her was Bonnie, the woman who seemed to know a lot about music. She was a younger woman who was the associate producer of a primetime television news program — one of those "60 Minutes" kinds of programs. I just knew *someone* else in this group had to be from California. We always seem to be the first to get in on the latest fad. She did have an interesting story, though. Ran away from her home in Alabama at age fifteen. Did drugs for fun and "the wild thing" for money. Some bleeding-heart street preacher took her under his wings and her life somehow got straightened out. Earned her GED, went to a community college, got a job with the network, and climbed her way up the ladder. Could be a "Movie of the Week."

The only other guy at the table was a certifiable "nerd." ("Bob's my name; computer science is my game," I was sure.) I half expected to see a plastic pocket-protector in his shirt pocket, but no such luck. Despite his ways, he was a pretty nice level-headed guy who seemed to know what questions he wanted answered. Turns out he's an orthopedic surgeon making rather large bucks. Go figure.

"Woman Number Three" was a "homemaker" named Mary Beth who admitted, somewhat hesitantly, that she hadn't experienced sex with her husband in almost eight months and couldn't understand why. I couldn't either. She was open enough, nice enough, smart enough, and pretty enough that if I weren't married, she could make it onto my short list. Must be something seriously wrong with their relationship. I hope for her sake he doesn't come home one night with some incurable sexually transmitted disease.

The last woman was invisible. Or at least she thought she was. I knew no more about her after dinner than I did before. She seemed interested in everyone else's life but didn't contribute anything about her own. But I wouldn't have to talk to her for a week, so what the heck?

After our wonderful but wineless meal, Tim stood up and addressed the group.

"I hope you've enjoyed getting to know one another, because as time goes on, you'll be asked to learn more about each other without actually talking among yourselves. Remember, from this moment on, you talk only to me. Now, this being your first night here, we're going to start off with the easy questions."

I glanced around the room. People were taking notes in their journals. I took that as an important clue and whipped out my pen. I hadn't even considered bringing my journal to dinner, so I wrote on what was left of my paper napkin. My first note? Bring journal to meals.

Tim continued. "Tonight, I want you to think about and write about three things: first, what are your personal goals for this retreat and for your life in general; second, what are your wishes or dreams for our world; and, finally, what do you wish for the people you met at your table tonight? If you get through all that, spend the rest of your evening developing a plan for world peace."

Give me a break! He didn't have to throw that last one in. At least he could have flagged it with a warning: "Sarcastic Semi-Humorous Comment Follows."

"Tomorrow, you're going to tell me, one-on-one, what you've written. Your point of reference on everything you write will be your personal experiences. My point of reference will be *The Message*, because it's the only wise and ancient teaching I've found that clearly tells who we are, where we have been and where we are going, and what we can become. It teaches us the path to God-Presence."

I wanted to stand up and say, "Tim, what is this Message bit? It sounds like another mystical manuscript that exists in someone's imagination, but not in reality. And what is this 'God-Presence'? Is it a 'he' or a 'she' or an 'it'? Is it a state of mind? Is it something you made up to give us mystical stories to tell when we get back home? I didn't come here to have someone pull something over on me. So don't try."

Of course, I said nothing. I sat there like everyone else. Twenty-two suckers on their way to some meaningless revelation for which we had paid rather large sums of money to discover. Just my airfare to this place had set me back nine hundred bucks. On top of that, a rental car and the "donation" to Tocayo "for services rendered."

I hate to sound so cynical. But I've had enough meaningless, contradictory, babbling garbage shoved down my throat to last a lifetime.

Everyone has answers, and I believe I've heard most of them. There are political answers, sociological answers, religious answers, psychological answers, scientific answers, economic answers, and even psychic answers.

Depending on who you talk to, all the solutions to the problems of the world can be attained by finding yourself, finding the worth in others, finding God, finding the truth, finding the right candidate for office, finding more money for everyone, or knowing the future just a wee bit ahead of time.

I was here to find my own answers, and I didn't feel I needed books, lectures, or ancient manuscripts to help me. I needed time...and time alone.

Still, if I planned to get anything out of my experience here, there would probably be some merit in going along with the entire program, including writing in my journal.

Tim dismissed us but said that we could sit in the dining room as long as we wanted. We were also free to go to the meeting hall, the library, or the meditation room if we didn't want to return to our cabins.

Since my journal was safely stashed away in my cabin, I decided to head back there. I wanted to get the first three questions out of the way so I could move on to the more important matter of world peace.

JOURNAL ENTRY — SUNDAY — MY FIRST DAY

I just became aware that I have stared at this page for almost twenty minutes and this is the first thing I'm writing.

I'm not sure why I'm here. But then, I'm not sure why I went to Sedona, Arizona, in April, or why I went to Teotihuacan, "The Place of the Gods," in Mexico, last fall.

I know I'm looking for something deeper than I've found in my existence to date, and I believe there's something to the energy of "spiritual centers." That's also why I seek out books that talk about spiritual experiences — not organized religions, just experiences.

I guess the strongest thing I'm feeling in my life is a sense of alienation.

I love my wife and children with all my heart, but I don't feel as close as I want to be. I feel as though some of my most private thoughts — disappointments and disillusionments — separate me from them, in either a psychological or a spiritual sense, I guess.

So my goal for this retreat and my life is to feel more connected. And to somehow discover how to feel more content with who I am, what I have, and what I've done with my life. I'm always comparing myself to others. Even at dinner, I looked at the congresswoman, Bonnie the "Hollywood" woman, and the orthopedic surgeon with some envy. And I have to admit I looked at "Woman Number Three" — I wish I could remember her name — with some lust. And I feel bad about that, too. Despite the occasional conflict with Connie, I'm basically a happily married man. I'm not supposed to undress strange women in my head.

My goal for the world? That's easy. I'd like to put an end to misery. At least the part of the misery that's caused by the human race. I know we can't do anything about earthquakes, hurricanes, fires, and other natural disasters that devastate so many lives. But I look at all the other things that have taken place just over the last few years — the strife in Northern Ireland, the inhumanity in Bosnia, the genocide in Rwanda, the L.A. riots, the World Trade Center bombing in New York — and I want to scream out, "Why do we keep doing these things to each other?"

Why do blacks hate whites, and whites hate blacks? Why do Arabs and Jews war with each other endlessly, no matter how many peace accords they sign? Why do Catholics, Protestants, and Muslims keep feeding their distrust and distaste for one another? Why do the peoples, the tribes and the nations of this world seek to conquer or destroy each other?

You'd think we would have learned enough from the hell-fires created by Hitler and the madmen who swore their allegiance to him. You'd think we could find a cure for the terrible diseases of hatred, bigotry, and greed. God, I hope so!

What do I wish for the others at my table? That they find what they're looking for, whether it's truth, satisfaction, or a relationship that makes a difference in their lives. I think about Connie's sister -- how lonely she is. How lost. She thinks that a single relationship with someone who matters is going to do it for her.

I'm not sure how much I'm supposed to write in this thing each time, so I'm quitting here.

Awakening to a New Day

I found it more difficult than I thought it would be to drift off to sleep. The reason was probably the utter lack of "ambient city noises" out here. No traffic. No horns. No police or fire sirens. No rattling trash cans. I don't even recall hearing an airplane flying overhead. I did hear a scratching sound just before I fell asleep; it was probably a small nocturnal animal of some sort looking for food.

Once asleep, I have to admit I slept well. I don't remember waking up once. Even though it was summer, the air in the cabin was rather cool, and the heavy quilt felt good. As corny as it sounds, it was almost womblike. Cold and cruel outside my covers, but warm and protected under them.

I fumbled a bit to find my watch on the desk, despite the fact that it was beginning to get light outside. Ten after six. According to the schedule, the wake-up chime wouldn't sound until 6:30, and breakfast wasn't until 8:00. I threw on some jeans and a great old sweatshirt and considered heading right for the shower but chose instead to walk down to the lake.

There was a low fog hanging over the trees on the far shore. In the distance, I could see someone fishing from a bright red canoe. There weren't any cabins or houses on this lake, I was told, but there must be a public access. In addition to the canoe, there were two small nonmotorized boats. I'm glad they respected the silence we all desired. Or at least they seemed to.

The wake-up chime rang right on schedule. That was the second time the chime had rung while I was down at the lake. And it had only rung twice since I'd been at Tocayo. If nothing else, that must mean I really do enjoy being by the water.

I stopped by my cabin to pick up my toiletry kit, and then headed for the shower building. I was not alone on this mission — everyone else seemed to be headed there at the same time. There were two entrances. Naturally, I chose the one labeled "MEN." I found an open mirror and sink and gave myself a quick shave, despite the fact I had vowed before coming here that I would take this opportunity to grow a beard, no matter how patchy it might look when I went back to work. The last time I had tried to grow one was in college, and there were some bare spots I couldn't seem to fill in. Maybe I'd fare better now.

There were only three shower stalls, so I had to wait my turn for a few minutes in a loosely organized queue. When I finally turned on the water in the shower, I was struck with my first major "insight" at Tocayo: "He who does not get to the shower without delay does not enjoy the benefits of hot water." It was a short shower. "A cup of good, hot, fresh coffee will sure help the situation," I thought.

I got dressed, dropped my toiletry kit in the cabin, grabbed my beloved journal, and headed to the main building.

Here's where I stumbled upon my second great insight. They

didn't have coffee here. No wine with dinner. No coffee with breakfast. Tim must have known this little fact would tick a lot of us off, because the first thing he said when he walked in the dining room was, "I'm sure some of you are wondering why we don't serve coffee with our meals. Well, very simply, we believe that caffeine is an addictive drug that can alter your natural state. We want you to be able to focus your thoughts as clearly as possible, so we don't provide caffeine or alcohol with any of our meals, and we discourage smoking on the grounds as well."

"Great, Tim," I wanted to say. "I NEED caffeine to think clearly. You're not going to *like* my 'natural state.' I won't even be fully awake before lunch if I don't get some coffee in my system." Still, I guess I could see his point.

I promised I wasn't going to go into detail describing our meals, but I'll tell you about our first breakfast because after that they were pretty much all the same. We had a lot of fruit — grapes, strawberries, raspberries, blueberries, melons, bananas, pineapple, peaches, and pears. We had whole-grain breads and corn bread, with natural preserves, but no butter or margarine. We had oatmeal and grits and a wide choice of juices. But no eggs, no bacon, no sausage, no ham — and milk was for the oatmeal only. Healthy, right? Well, I knew that by the third day I'd be hiking the twelve miles into town for an Egg McMuffin.

Breakfast was also accompanied by recorded music. Because we couldn't speak, I tried to catch the glances of the others at my table, to see if I could tell how they were doing with all of this. It's amazing how much we must all rely on language to communicate, because I couldn't really discern much of anything by looking at the others. Maybe I was just too new at this. (Bonnie seemed to look a little less stressed out, though.)

After breakfast, we gathered in the meeting room for a "seminar." According to the schedule, it would last an hour, and then we'd have our private conferences with Tim.

Tim's first crack at a seminar lasted less than five minutes.

"All I'm going to do this morning is read a short story to you." He opened a book that was sitting on the podium and began.

"There was once a man who had two sons. The younger said to his father, 'Father, I want right now what's coming to me.'

"So the father divided the property between them. It wasn't long before the younger son packed his bags and left for a distant country. There, undisciplined and dissipated, he wasted everything he had. After he had gone through all his money, there was a bad famine all through that country, and he began to hurt. He signed on with a citizen there who assigned him to his fields to slop the pigs. He was so hungry he would have eaten the corncobs in the pig slop, but no one would give him any.

"That brought him to his senses. He said, 'All those farmhands working for my father sit down to three meals a day, and here I am starving to death. I'm going back to my father. I'll say to him, "I don't deserve to be called your son. Take me on as a hired hand.' " He got up right away and went home to his father.

"When he was still a long way off, his father saw him..."

Tim paused. "I'm going to stop the story right there because I want each of you to imagine what happened next. What did the young man's father do? Did he say, 'Serves you right, you arrogant jerk!' Did he say, 'Get out of my sight. I don't want you back here ever again'? Did he take him on as a hired hand?

"What would you do? What would you say?"

Tim headed toward the door at the back of the room. "In case you're wondering, I'll finish the story later. The outcome may surprise you."

Something about this story sounded vaguely familiar, but I couldn't put my finger on it. I sat for a few moments thinking about Tim's questions, as did most of the others. Slowly, one by one, we left the room.

My first stop was Tim's office, where I noted that my first private conference was scheduled for 11:15 that morning. I contemplated going to the library until the appointed time but chose to return to my cabin.

⬥

The sound of the chime woke me from a deep sleep. The sunlight was streaming in through the window from a high angle, so I knew it wasn't the morning wake-up chime. Besides, I was fully dressed.

Panic struck me as I checked my watch. It was 12:30 in the afternoon. That was the lunch chime I heard. Oh, no! I had missed my 11:15 conference with Tim. Worse, I hadn't given any thought to the story he told. I decided I must be more drained from the stresses of life than I thought.

I wondered what the punishment was for skipping a conference. Maybe they'd force coffee down my throat! After all, missing my morning cup (or three) was probably why I had missed my morning conference.

My pace was fairly brisk as I directed my feet in the direction of the lodge. I tried to slip past Tim on my way into the dining hall, but he was too quick for me.

"Your conferences are among the most important of all your activities here," he scolded. "I'm not going to let you off the hook, Jeff. I have an open slot right after lunch, and I want to see you there." I nodded.

Despite the fact that I couldn't talk to the others at my table, I could sense that they were beginning to feel a calming effect from the retreat. The worry lines were disappearing from their faces, and they seemed more willing to smile. Bonnie *really* looked destressed. If one day here could have such a noticeable impact, I could only imagine how we'd all look and feel after a full week.

I promised I would drop the "menu report" from my account, so I'm going to. But let's just say that every morsel was "healthy." I almost allowed myself the thought that this place was really a Fat Farm disguised as a spiritual retreat. At any rate, it wouldn't hurt for me to lose the love handles and lower my cholesterol, so I might as well shut up and enjoy my veggies.

After I finished my nutritious lunch, I made my way down the narrow hallway to Tim's office. The door was open, and he was already seated behind his desk.

"Come in, Jeff. Have a chair." Tim motioned me in and looked in the direction of the only open chair in the room. I glanced around as surreptitiously as I could. Pretty simple office, I thought. No phone, no fax machine, no copier, no files. Just a desk, Tim's chair, my chair, a small table with an ugly lamp on it, and a tall bookshelf filled with books. Some of the books appeared to be very old. Some were very new; among them some of the hottest "spiritual" best sellers of recent times.

"How are things going so far?" Tim asked.

I didn't have a good answer, so I gave a stock one. "Okay, I think. I'm looking forward to getting a lot out of the experience."

"Self-actualization? Personal fulfillment? That sort of thing? Is that what you're hoping for?" he asked.

"Yes, I guess so. I've looked a lot of places for answers — even had my 'mountaintop experiences' you might say."

"Well, I hate to say this, but you might have come to the wrong place for the wrong reasons."

I was puzzled by that admission but said nothing as he continued.

"We're more about giving, and forgiving, and putting others first, and searching for and finding a higher energy that can make these goals practical and attainable. We seek to turn our back on self-centeredness and find a true spirituality."

"Why?" I asked. "Why would this work?"

"Because, Jeff, all of the 'me first' philosophies haven't worked. People strive with all their energy to fulfill themselves. They buy things they think will make them happy. New cars, big houses, fast boats, you name it. They make and break relationships — often casually — in search of that one person whom they feel can best meet their needs. They change mates and careers and friends like they were socks. And they still come up empty." He paused and looked straight at me. "What do you think? Is there some truth in what I'm saying, or am I full of it?"

"Yes, there's truth there," I admitted. "But I'm basically satisfied with my life — my achievements, my wife and family, my home, my friends. Except..."

"Except," Tim jumped in, "there's something missing from the puzzle and you don't know what it is."

"Well, yeah, right." I decided this guy didn't need to know *everything* about me and my life.

"Where have you looked for the missing piece?" he asked.

"Um, I've read a lot. I've spent time trying to get in touch with nature. I've been to some of the global centers of spiritual energy. Not all of them, but some of them. I've sought the advice of counselors. And I've looked within myself." I hesitated, not knowing what to expect, then asked, "Anything wrong with all of that?"

Tim had a genuine look on his face, so I believed what he said next. "I'm not here to judge or criticize any of the paths you've traveled in the past. Each of us has to make our own journey. I'm here only to be your guide on a new path. It's up to you to decide if you want to take it. *The Message* says it's a narrow path, and there are very few who will find it."

"What do you mean?"

"Jeff, you remember the story I told in the seminar today? About the young man who took his inheritance, squandered it in wild partying, and ended up living with the pigs?"

I nodded.

"Well," he continued, "the path he chose was to return to his father. There are a lot of good reasons he could have decided otherwise. Pride, for example. Or doubts about whether or not his father really loved him and would accept him back into the family. Or maybe even the hope that he could rebuild his life on his own."

"But we still don't know what happened when he returned," I added.

"Right!" Tim said. "Maybe his next step was to ask his father for forgiveness. Then it would all be up to his father — whether to forgive him or not."

I was starting to get suspicious. "This all sounds a little like conventional religion to me. You know. Do wonderful deeds, be a good Boy Scout, and ask the Almighty for forgiveness and mercy."

"I hope it doesn't sound like that, because it isn't."

"Good."

"Why do you say that, Jeff? Is there something in particular about religion that you don't like?"

"Plenty," I said as I went over the list in my mind. "Repression, greed, narrow-mindedness. I could go on and on."

"I want you to. In fact," he proposed, "I want you to take on an added assignment. I'd like you to write your thoughts on religion in your journal. It can be any religion. Ones you know about. Or others you don't but just have feelings about. Or just general observations on religious beliefs and practices as a whole."

"What do I gain by doing this?"

"Nothing, perhaps. But it seems to be something you need to express."

"What about my journal entry from last night? You know, my goals for myself? My hopes for the world and for the other people here?"

"We'll get to that at the right time. But those are things you may want to rethink before we talk about them."

With that, Tim stood up. "I have others waiting. I'm sorry. But our meeting tomorrow will be very important and I'm looking forward to it."

I walked out of Tim's office and headed straight for my cabin, with some anger building up inside me. These writing assignments were starting to tick me off. And this last one was totally annoying. "You want my thoughts on 'religion'? This won't be good — but you asked for it, Timmy-Boy."

I took out my checkbook, tore out a deposit ticket, and began working on a rough outline of my thoughts. I wanted to develop the clearest presentation that I could before committing my thoughts to the pages of my journal, and this seemed like the best way to do it. I was deeply engrossed when the chime rang. It was too early for dinner, so I knew it meant our afternoon seminar was next on the agenda. I tucked my deposit ticket into my journal and set out for the lodge. I stopped just outside my door, my instincts telling me there was something I'd forgotten. Then it hit me: usually when I walk out of my house, I make sure I lock the door. But no key, no lock, so no need.

I settled in my chair and waited for the stragglers to walk in. Tim must have had some private vantage point where he could watch us all arrive, because at both seminars he'd managed to enter the room just seconds after the last person got seated.

"I imagine you've all had an opportunity to think about the story I told you this morning," Tim began. "And I imagine that each of you has, or could have, written the next chapter to the story. Undoubtedly, every one of them would have been different. One of you may have written that when the son returned home, his father said, 'You can come back, but there won't be any more inheritance for you ever, because you've blown it.' Another of you may have concluded that the father said something like, 'You made your bed, now go sleep in it.' Still another might suggest that the father refused to even see the son — that he told his servants to send him back where he came from. Or you could suggest that the father forgave his son for squandering his wealth and said, 'Welcome home, son. Now get to work and prove that you can do things right and contribute to our estate through hard work.' "

Tim looked around the room. "Now," he said, "I'd like you to raise your hand if your outcome for the story matches any of those I've suggested."

Well over half of the hands went up — including mine — though I didn't know which scenario had entered the minds of the various other individuals. For my part, I thought the father would want the son to get back into the "family business" and contribute skill and hard work to its ongoing success. After all, the son owed it to his father, I believe. And this would be the perfect opportunity to demonstrate his worth.

Tim flipped through his book, settled on a page, and said, "*The Message* completes the story this way: '*When the son was still a long way off, his father saw him. His heart pounding, he ran out, embraced him, and kissed him.*'"

"I think," Tim continued, "that this story is telling us something important. The young man's father was watching for, hoping for, even expecting the return of his son. The father saw him when he was still a long way off — while the son thought all along that he would be forever alienated from his father, and that he could hope to be no more than a hired hand. His father ran out to him, his heart pounding with excitement, and greeted him with open arms."

Tim paused, looking for feedback from our expressions, then went on. "We discover in the story a solution to the age-old problem of alienation."

"What's going on here?" I thought to myself. "Did this guy sneak into my cabin and read my journal while I was sleeping? Why else would the subject of 'alienation' come up?"

"Alienation can be a two-way problem, where each party resists the other," Tim added. "Resolution in these cases is very difficult, if not impossible. But most alienation in our world, if you are open enough to look at it honestly, is a one-way problem. It exists in the mind of only one individual. It can be imagined or it can be real. It can be the result of fear — of what the other person might think or do or say — or it can simply be a kind of 'holding back.' Perhaps that kind of individual doesn't want to be known.

We all experience alienation in some form, and we experience it to some degree with every other person in our lives. Until some external circumstance comes into play to force the isolated individual to make a move, other individuals will never have the opportunity to welcome the alienated person into their lives — or to welcome them back. In our story, it was poverty and hunger — utter destitution — that forced the son to re-evaluate his condition. His father was always willing to accept him and welcome him. The son didn't have to work his way back into his father's good graces. He was loved — completely and unselfishly.

"There's even more to the story," Tim concluded. "But I want you to think about any alienation that exists in your life. Is it 'one way' or 'two way'? If you're the one who's alienated, what would it take to move you toward reconciliation? You realize, I'm sure, that the son's pride could have prevented him from returning to his father. Pride is a powerful force. None of us likes to admit we are wrong. Maybe the guiding question has to be, 'What is a relationship worth?' "

Tim walked out and Michael stood up in front to announce the schedule for the next day and to remind us to make sure we had signed up for our private conference. Then he dismissed us until dinner.

I was a little confused. Was I supposed to work on the original assignment Tim had given me, or was I supposed to turn my attention and energy to the question of one-way versus two-way alienation? My mind was racing as I walked the path back to my cabin. Tim didn't actually tell us to *write* about the alienation topic; he asked us to *think* about it. I opened the door, walked in, sat down at the desk, opened my journal, and pulled out my deposit ticket. I'd tackle religion first.

JOURNAL ENTRY — MONDAY AFTERNOON

Someone once said, "If you can't say something good, don't say anything." Well, I'm the wrong guy to ask about religion. To me, religion represents four things: rules, guilt, shame, and hypocrisy.

Rules first, because that's where it started for me. I grew up in a very conservative "Christian" home. We went to church every Sunday. That was Rule Number One. Rule Number Two was we sat quietly when we were supposed to be quiet, sang when we were supposed to sing, prayed when we were supposed to pray, and knelt when we were supposed to kneel. There was no room for original thinking here. Rule Number Three was the "all-in-one" rule — the rule to end all rules — the only other rule you needed: if it's fun, you can't do it. No movies, no dancing, no playing cards, and, of course, no sex. Or kissing or fondling or any other activity that could possibly, under any circumstances, lead to sex. No wonder I gave up church when I got to college. And discovered movies, dancing, cards, and sex.

Guilt is next. And we had enough of it in our family to go around for everyone. I have some Jewish friends who make jokes about their "Jewish mothers" — an unfair and undeserved stereotype, I think, because my Protestant mother fits their descriptions exactly. Actually, in most cases, I would have traded them — mother for mother.

My belief is that we're supposed to enjoy life, not feel some self-imposed or God-imposed guilt about everything we do, think, or say. Show me a religion without all the guilt crud, and maybe we could talk.

Then there's something that follows close on the heels of guilt, and that's good old shame. Hey, I know I've done a few things wrong in my life, but I don't need to go back to church week after week to hear how I've failed. I ran across some books that helped, though. One of them opened my eyes to the crud I'd put up with in church over the years. I could see that there was a mountain of shame mixed in with the "old-time religion." I never knew it at the time, but I guess that's why Dad would come home from church looking all depressed instead of feeling better about himself and his world. No matter what we did or didn't do, we were wrong and awful and despicable and detestable. We tried, but we were never "Christian" enough — never good enough. Church was full of it — if they couldn't nail us for the things we had done wrong, at least they could make us feel like trash. No thank you!

The real biggie though — the "religion buster" — is hypocrisy. Most of these people preach one thing and practice another.

Seems like every time you turn on the news, another big-time TV evangelist has been caught with his pants down at some off-the-beaten-path motel. These guys seem to drop like flies. As do their shorts.

I have to wonder: is it fame that's gone to their heads? Are they lonely? Is there something missing in their relationships at home? Or are they just selfish slimeballs? It doesn't matter. Because the whole point is, they talk virtue from their pulpits, and then talk sweet-nothings in the ears of unsuspecting young women who trust them. And the ones who aren't in it for sex are in it for the money. Total garbage, if you ask me.

Here's another one: "Pro-life." Give me a break, okay? How can someone claim to be anti-abortion/pro-life, and then gun down a doctor in front of an abortion clinic? And the next day the killer wears a proud smile all the way to the courtroom? All in the name of religion.

I'm not venting my feelings on just Christians, either. They're all screwed up. In India, the cows live and the kids die. In Iran, they consider it an honor to kill someone of another religion in the mighty name of "Allah." Who knows what they do in Bora-Bora! Probably blood sacrifices, for all I know.

Get my point, Tim? Religion is worthless. I probably can't and shouldn't say that about all people who practice religion. I've met nice Christians and Jews and Muslims and Hindus. But I hope they depend more on themselves than on their "gods." The gods seem to steer them wrong and let them down.

The Debate

As irritated as I was all of Monday afternoon and throughout dinner (on top of everything else, we had bland Mexican food, if you can imagine such a thing), I woke up early, feeling rested, and I knew I wouldn't miss my morning coffee as much as I had yesterday. It was still nearly an hour and a half until breakfast, so I considered my options. I could be the first in the shower and assure myself of hot water. I could go out for a walk, but it was a chilly morning and my shoes would likely get wet from the dew that had settled on the tall grass. Somehow, staying on the defined paths didn't appeal to me. Or I could write in my Journal. Given the lack of additional realistic options (picking up a sack of donuts at the 7-Eleven was out of the question, and even if I headed down the hill now, I still wouldn't beat the early risers to the hot water), I picked up my journal and pen.

JOURNAL ENTRY — THIRD DAY — TUESDAY MORNING
I can hardly wait to share my thoughts on religion

with Tim. My first priority is to get on his conference schedule as early as possible.

I'm kind of ticked that he didn't want to hear my thoughts on my goals for the retreat and my sterling plans for the world-at-large. I thought it was pretty good stuff.

I hope that before this week is over, we can skip this peripheral nonsense and get to the real issues — things I've been thinking about since junior high. Why are we here? What is our purpose in life? How can we find true happiness and satisfaction for ourselves? Where do we go from here? You know...the simple things.

I couldn't think of anything else to write at the moment, so I shaved, took my shower, and headed for the library to wait out the chime for breakfast. I was the only one in the room. I was examining the shelves from left to right, top to bottom, in an anal-retentive sort of way, looking for something to catch my eye, when Tim walked in.

"Good morning, Jeff. It appears you are the first person this week to discover my little secret. I had the place all to myself yesterday."

I must have looked puzzled.

He laughed. "I come here every morning — usually a lot earlier than this. It's about the only quiet time I get until after dinner."

I saw he was carrying his dilapidated copy of *The Message*. I calculated that he must spend time reading it in the morning. I asked, "Am I allowed to be in this room? Is it okay to talk to you in here?"

"Well, of course you can be here," he replied, "although, technically, we're not supposed to talk. But you somehow impress me as having more on your mind than most of the others here, so I don't have a problem with that."

I hesitated, groping for the right thing to say. "Do you mind if I share my thoughts on religion now, so that we can talk about something more important in our conference?"

"No," he said, "that would be fine with me."

I opened my journal to the appropriate page and handed it to him. Then I sat kind of nervously in my chair and studied his face as he read. He finished and closed the book.

"What do you think?" I asked.

His response was matter-of-fact. "It's pretty much what I expected. Most people have similar views on religion, especially if they were force-fed it when they were young. Anyone who has an ax to grind on the topic usually says roughly the same things."

"So you've given this assignment before?"

"Only when I think it could actually help someone work through some issues."

I got defensive. "Well, it's not an 'issue' for me. I've settled the entire matter in my mind."

"I understand."

Now I was getting steamed, "So you don't think my point of view is legitimate? You don't think it's valid?"

Tim didn't seem at all ruffled by my outburst. "Of course I think it's legitimate. You raise some excellent points. I'm just telling you it's typical. Standard issue. I know. I've heard these views expressed by others before you. And I read the newspapers. I know about 'fallen TV evangelists.' I've seen more hypocrisy than I care to recall. And I know about rules and routine and ritual. But, fortunately, getting to understand and know the God-Presence has absolutely nothing to do with religion. Any religion. God-Presence is Light — all of these things you've written about are Darkness. And Light and Darkness can't exist in the same place at the same time."

This was making no sense, and obviously, the look on my face encouraged him to continue. He flipped through his book and read me a few paragraphs.

"What it says in a later revelation, Jeff, is that Light has streamed into the world, but men and women everywhere ran for the darkness; that they are *'addicted to denial and illusion'* — those are the exact words — and won't come near the light, fearing painful exposure."

I interrupted. "So what you're saying is that this light is the God-Presence?"

"Yes," he went on. "The Light exposes our self-centeredness — the one thing that has destroyed our relationships and alienated us from each other, from nature, and from God-Presence. Self-centeredness is the perfect breeding ground for distrust, fear, and all those other negative emotions, because we want to protect ourselves from hurt no matter what the cost. That's the real cause of all the ethnic problems, and the crime, and war. It's not because someone else looks different, or thinks different, or acts different, or worships different, or wears different clothes and listens to a different style of music."

"So, this alienation you talk about," I asked, knowing full well what his answer would be, "do we all experience it? Is it a universal human condition?"

He responded with a question, which caught me off guard:

"Do you believe in the story of Creation?"

I laughed. "You mean Adam and Eve and the Garden of Eden and all that stuff? I think I might have in the first grade."

"Okay," he said. "Let's say we don't believe a word of it, although strong scientific and historical cases can be made for both sides of this issue — belief and suspension of belief in favor of other evidence. But let's just call it an allegory of the human experience. If the Garden did exist, we can probably assume it was an idyllic spot — two young people, a man and a woman, frolicking around naked, partaking of all the wonders of Creation...enjoying uninhibited sex, eating lush fruits hanging from every tree, experiencing intimate companionship with the animals. There was no pollution, no strip mining, no greed, no envy. They had everything they wanted or needed in this extraordinary place, which I imagine to be the most magnificent rain forest ever possible. They even had communion with someone referred to as their Creator-God."

"I've heard this whole story," I interjected. "A snake came along, right? And they ate the apple and were banished from the kingdom. Remember, I'm the guy who was dragged to church as a kid..."

"Well, you sort of have it right. One day, a spiritual enemy of the Creator-God, an angel of darkness, came into the Garden and tempted them with something they didn't have — the knowledge of good and evil, which at that time belonged exclusively to the Creator-God."

I *had* to speak up. "Oh, please! Nobody in their right mind buys this old legend."

"Jeff, I told you at the outset that you don't have to believe a single word. I'm simply using this as an illustration of a greater lesson."

I was on Tim's time, so I decided to listen. "Go ahead. I'm sorry."

"No problem. Here's the point. They gave in to the spiritual enemy and took a bite of the fruit — it wasn't an apple, actually, it was something even more wonderful — and instantly they knew they had turned their backs on the Creator-God and all that love and communion that was theirs. That was the moment when the alienation we all feel today first came into being. From that moment forward, alienation ruled. Shortly thereafter, the first murder was committed — a brother killing his brother. And since that time, our species has been at war. War among nations, war among races, and private little wars in our own homes. That's the price of alienation."

"Is this story in *The Message*?" I asked.

"No, actually, *The Message* is a later manuscript. But here's what it does say. It does say that *'all the broken and dislocated pieces of the universe — people and things, animals and atoms — get properly fixed and fit together in vibrant harmonies'* because of the Light of the God-Presence. It says that God-Presence tears down the walls we use to keep each other at a distance, that the Light brings an end to hostilities."

I hate to admit it to myself, but I was starting to get into this. Our conversation was interrupted by the breakfast chime, and we both got up to leave.

"I'd be glad to talk with you more about this later," Tim said.

My reply surprised even me. "I would, too."

Our first seminar that day was scheduled to begin immediately following breakfast. Despite the fact that I took my time and studied the faces of the others at my table while I ate, I still finished well before the seminar starting time.

I got up, smiled at everyone, and walked outside. As I looked at the surroundings, I wondered to myself, "Where *did* all this come from?" The "Big Bang" theory of the origin of the universe held great weight with me. But for a moment I entertained the thought that perhaps a "Creator-God" could have been the force behind the Big Bang. But that still doesn't explain away evolution. And my studies of it in college were far too in-depth to allow me to dismiss it. Fortunately, as Tim pointed out, I didn't have to believe in a Creator-God to catch the implications of his story. I could clearly see that alienation was at the root of our problems throughout history — wherever it came from.

The chime announcing the start of the seminar sounded, and I left the peacefulness of the outdoors for the stuffy atmosphere of the meeting room. I wondered why they didn't hold some of these seminars outside on the grounds.

Tim had been seated along the outside wall near the front of the room. He stood up and walked slowly to the podium. For the longest time, he didn't say anything. One by one, he caught our eyes — each of us individually — and looked into them for a moment. I felt a little uncomfortable with this.

Finally he spoke. "You're wondering why I took the time to look at each of you. I wanted to find out what I could see simply by looking at you, and I wanted to know what I was feeling toward you. And Bernie, I want you to know that even though you're vision-impaired, this worked with you, too, because I can see well past the darkness that clouds your eyes. Now, *I* know what I'm feeling, but I'm not going to share those thoughts right now. I want you to gather into a small group with the people from your dining room table and take the next twenty minutes looking at each others eyes. Look into the other faces, one at a time, and see what you can read in them. Then think about what you feel about them."

Twenty minutes! He had to be kidding! That would seem like forever. Nonetheless, I was interested in doing this little exercise because I hadn't been able to talk to the group since our first dinner. I recalled what Tim had said on that occasion — that as time went on, we'd be asked to learn more about each other without actually talking among ourselves. This must be what he meant.

We found an open spot and drew our chairs into a small circle. I first paired off with Bonnie, the television producer from my "home town." I think we both must have had an embarrassed look on our faces, because we both kind of grinned. But I took this assignment seriously and began to search her eyes and study her face.

As I looked at her, an amazing thing happened. Her eyes became more round and open. Her face became softer and more beautiful. She almost seemed to glow. When I had first met her, I thought she was "hard looking" — probably the result of her rough years as a runaway. But now I saw a different dimension — almost as if all the bad things in her life had been erased by some miraculous experience. I didn't know if it was something that was taking place right now, or had occurred on this retreat, or had happened at some earlier time in her life. But the evidence seemed to be visible in her eyes, and it was almost as if she wanted to communicate it to me. I enjoyed looking at her; it gave me a sense of peace.

We knew instinctively, without being told, when it was time to change partners. The congresswoman was next. I saw strain on her face. This retreat had appeared to calm her some, but there was the look of much unfinished business in her eyes. It was almost an "I've got to get out of here — now!" message that she was sending me. I wondered if being a member of Congress — of having all the responsibility of helping shape the future direction of an entire country — was the cause for that look. Through my eyes, I tried to send her the peace and calm I had gained from Bonnie.

Next, it was my turn for the surgeon. I remembered his name to be John, though I wasn't sure. As I studied him, I noticed he had a "wise" look (I half expect that of a medical doctor; it would put my mind at ease if I ever had to see him professionally), though he didn't seem to be particularly at peace with himself either. I wondered if any of us would be further along in our lives after spending a week at the Habitat. "Doctor John" sure didn't seem to be making any progress. His gaze seemed very distant, almost as if he didn't really want to study me in return.

Then, I moved on to the "Invisible Woman." Only this time she didn't seem invisible. She communicated more with her eyes than she had with her words, or lack of them, at our first dinner. I saw a mixture of hurt and fear in her eyes, as if she had just gone through a traumatic experience and was terrified of what could happen to her next. I could tell she was trying to mask her feelings and keep them to herself, but it wasn't working. They rushed to the surface in waves with each searching glance.

Last, but certainly not least, was Mary Beth, the woman who had shared some of her marital hurts. Her eyes seemed to say, "Please! Won't someone please pay attention to me? Won't someone acknowledge my existence?" Then it occurred to me that I was probably reading that message into our communication because of what she had told the group at our first encounter. But the longer I looked at her, the more I realized that *was* her message — her only message — and she was willing and eager to communicate it any way she could. I really hoped for her, above all the others, that this retreat would be a genuine turning point for her. I guess I felt that way because her message was so clear. So I knew what to hope for.

I wondered if everyone else had seen the same things in the eyes and expressions of the others, or if I had received special messages reserved only for me. I couldn't believe the thoughts that were forming in my mind. I didn't feel any sense of alienation at this moment. In fact, I felt something I could almost describe as a form of love. A primitive form, perhaps, but still real.

We remained in our circle for a few minutes, casting glances at each other. Some of the other groups hadn't finished the exercise, so Tim waited to resume the seminar.

When all of the groups appeared to have finished, Tim stood up again and said, "When we've done this exercise in the past, I've had people tell me one of two things in the conferences that follow. A few people — very few, actually — tell me that they spent most of their time worrying about what they were communicating. They wanted to know what the others thought, and because of that, they couldn't receive the messages intended for them. That's a form of self-centeredness, though certainly not the most serious form I've encountered. So if you felt that way, don't punish yourself. Don't beat yourself up. That doesn't make you 'bad.' "

He went on. "The overwhelming response I hear after this exercise is that people become 'connected' with each other in a new way. The feeling of alienation disappears, and a sense of well-being takes its place. Some participants have gone so far as to call those feelings 'love.' "

"Now I *know* this guy reads minds," I thought.

Tim walked around to the front of the podium, presumably to get closer to us — for what reason, I was never sure.

"I have an assignment for you. And it's one of the most important ones I'm going to give you. So important, in fact, that I'm going to cancel our other seminar today, and if you think you can get along without your conference, I'd like you to cancel that as well. Just spend your time thinking and writing."

This guy was full of contradictions. First he told me that our private conferences were among our most important activities, and then he, in effect, suspended them in favor of thinking and writing. "What could be that important?" I wondered. Did he just want a day off from his duties?

"Love is the question," Tim continued. "What is it? Does it endure? Can it be described? Can it be created on command? Does it only exist when it's returned? These are the things I want you to consider. I promise it will be worth your time."

After Tim left the room, I and several others, including everyone in my group, sat in our places for a while, not quite knowing how to proceed. I finally decided that the best place to think and write would be in my cabin. That way, I could take short breaks down by the lake, though I was certain everyone else would have the same idea.

On the way back to my cabin, I noticed that the clouds had thickened up quite a bit, and it looked like it could rain. "Doesn't really matter much to me if it does," I thought.

Love and Its Counterparts

Every time I glanced up from my journal, it appeared that the sky had gotten a little darker. The air coming in my window had that moist scent it often has just before the rains begin.

The next time I looked up from my writing, it was because I heard thunder in the distance. It sounded as if it was coming from the southwest — in the direction of the far side of the lake. As the thunder became louder, the winds picked up, and it started to rain. It pounded against the roof and sides of my cabin, and I had to close the window to keep my desk and bed from getting soaked.

The thunder never got any louder after that. From the shift in direction of the sound, the heaviest part of the storm appeared to have missed us, and headed southeast. The wind died down very suddenly, and all that was left was a gentle rain that fell straight to the ground. I opened my window because I knew I would no longer risk getting wet and damaging my "treasured journal." I could still hear the thunder in the distance, but the threat of severe weather seemed remote, and the sky was getting lighter.

I once again became absorbed in my writing.

Twenty minutes later, when everything came unglued, it became abundantly clear to me why I had not gone into the field of weather forecasting. The sky had become unbelievably black. The lightning flashes were blinding, and the thunder followed almost instantly on their heels. I remembered from old science classes that because sound travels much slower than light — about a thousand feet a second, I think — if five seconds elapsed between the flash and the sound, the lightning would be approximately a mile away. When the next flash burst, not even a second elapsed. It was so close, I had the sudden urge to take cover under the bed.

"If there is a Creator-God," I thought, "he or she did not exhibit very good judgment in creating things as deadly as thunderstorms, hurricanes, earthquakes, and tornadoes." I can't comprehend the energy that is unleashed by these natural phenomena.

I was amazed I could hear the faint sound of the 12:30 lunch chime in the midst of the relentless fury of that sudden storm. There was no way I was going to venture out in that madness; I'd probably get hit by a falling tree if I did. Besides, I wasn't hungry, and I had things to say that had not yet found their way onto paper.

JOURNAL ENTRY— TUESDAY AFTERNOON

I'm actually starting to like the idea of keeping this journal. For one thing, it helps me remember the questions I want to bring up to Tim. For another, it will help me replay my experiences to others who may be interested in visiting this place and perhaps embarking on what Tim calls "a journey to freedom from alienation and self-centeredness." I wonder if anyone has ever completed this journey.

That thought aside, the issue of the day is love. And I believe this is one thing I've finally gotten a pretty good handle on in recent years.

With all the talk about love in movies, on TV, and in music, it still seems that we're missing out on two key elements of what love probably ought to be: commitment and unselfishness.

In a way, it gets back to the thing Tim has been talking about: self-centeredness. But I believe that it's possible for me to have *my* best interests at heart and still be committed and unselfish in my love relationships — with my wife, my children, and perhaps even with others.

I remember when I was in college, everyone believed that every relationship called "love" could only be fully and completely expressed in bed. That was the philosophy of the 70s that many of us still bought into in the 80s. I was buying it, too, because it sure beat the heck out of celibacy.

But I can't even remember the names of some of the young women I "loved" back then. So much for commitment. Or unselfishness, for that matter.

I've changed considerably since my college years, and so have a lot of the others of my generation, as well as the generation that has followed. Now, with the reality of AIDS and other sexually transmitted diseases facing us square in the face, the pace of "free love" out there has slowed down some. Looks like the fear of death is sort of a breeding ground for commitment.

So the question I keep turning over in my mind is, what is love really? And how can I love without it turning into a sexual thing? Is there a higher kind of love where commitment and unselfishness operate? And is it as satisfying as — or possibly even more satisfying than — the kind of relationship that results in an orgasm?

I'm past the point where I want to sleep with everyone who breathes and wears a skirt. But, as a result of our exercise earlier today, I'm feeling the closest thing to love that I possibly can about the others in my group — a deep, sincere concern.

Maybe all I'm feeling about my group is the "warm fuzzies." Maybe it's something more. I know it's not sexual. I know I don't have to undress in a darkened room to express it. I also know I want to learn more about what it is and how to demonstrate it to the "objects of my love." And have them demonstrate their love to me in return.

✦

I was very proud of my journal entry on the meaning of love and was anxious to report my thoughts to Tim. The next morning, I skipped breakfast and arrived at his office well ahead of my scheduled time. I wanted to make sure I got every minute I had coming to me. I imagined his face beaming with pride as he read my "breakthrough" words.

"There are some astute observations here," Tim noted as he read my brilliant, well-conceived work. "I'm pleased to see you've gotten well past the notion that love is somehow represented by genital sex and can only be expressed in the privacy of the bedroom. I'm also glad you realize that there can be love between people of the same sex that does not have to indicate same-sex preference. But all your explanations just touch on the surface of what love really is — or what it could be in a God-Present world."

The first thought that cropped up was, "Oh, goodie! Here we go again with that Message garbage. Aren't there other valid points of view? Does it — can it — all come out of one old, worn-out book?"

But what I said was, "Does *The Message* have something to say about it?"

"Indeed," said Tim. "But few accept its teaching."

"What does it teach?" I inquired, knowing full well there was no preventing the answer anyway.

"It says that love is more than 'warm fuzzies.' More than the desire to give so that you can receive some similar expression in return. Seeking some benefit from love, no matter how nonspecific, is still self-centeredness, and still ultimately leads to alienation. *The Message* clearly says that the very best way to love is to put your life on the line for your friends. To actually be willing to die for them. When you die, you see, you get nothing in return. But I know so few who have been willing to express love to that degree. It is rare indeed."

"Do you know *anyone* like that?" I asked.

"Some," he responded. "And I've read about some. A number of years ago, in the mid-seventies, I believe, there was a book called *The Hiding Place*. It was made into a movie, too. It was the true story of a Dutch woman — a watchmaker and her family — who risked everything to hide Jews from the Nazis in a small secret room in their house. They didn't even know most of the people whose lives they saved, yet they put it all on the line in the name of love. The woman's name was Corrie ten Boom. They were all arrested. Her sister and her father died in prison. But she was somehow released from a terrible concentration camp, and she spent the last years of her life traveling around the world telling people about this kind of love."

"This all sounds very idealistic," I said. "But the reality is that most of us have families — wives or husbands and children — and it's very irresponsible to go around offering to die for other people. I know my wife would be pretty upset if I called her up and said, 'Honey, I'm sorry, but I won't be home tonight. I have to go die for my friend Bob.' "

"Jeff, I'm not telling you to go out and actively seek a friend to die for. What I'm talking about is attitude — your willingness to put those you love ahead of yourself. It's what you've already described in two words — unselfishness and commitment. But I'm not sure you understand the full meaning of those words. Listen to how *The Message* describes the qualities of love."

Tim turned to a point about two thirds of the way through his book and began to read.

"Love never gives up.
Love cares more for others than for self.
Love doesn't want what it doesn't have.
Love doesn't strut,
Doesn't have a swelled head,
Doesn't force itself on others,
Isn't always 'me first,'

Doesn't fly off the handle,
Doesn't keep score of the sins of others,
Doesn't revel when others grovel, and
Takes pleasure in the flowering of truth.
LOVE NEVER FAILS."

Tim put down his book and looked straight in my eyes. "Don't you think part of the reason the world isn't the idyllic place we all want it to be is because we want to redefine love as sex, as pleasure-on-demand, or as a philosophy that either says 'if you love me first, then I'll love you,' or 'if I love myself first, my love for you will naturally follow'?"

"Could be," I acknowledged. "But I'm beyond that, at least by your interpretation of my journal entry."

"I'm going to give you a tough assignment," Tim said.

"They've all been tough, Tim," I commented, the sarcasm in my voice not too well masked.

"No," he said, "they've all been bubbling on the surface. If you can answer this one, you're on your way to a profound insight. The question I want you to think about and write about is, 'Who are you willing to die for?' Who do you love *that* much, Jeff?"

With that, Tim stood up, walked over to the door, and opened it for me. "Sorry to have to end this, but I have another appointment."

I stepped into the hallway and noticed Mary Beth, journal in hand, fidgeting in her usual manner. She must have been the next in line. Indeed she was; Tim invited her into his office with a simple welcoming look.

I decided the thing to do was to skip my morning walk, head straight for my cabin, and write in my journal. Something inside told me this was not going to be easy...especially if I was serious about such matters as honesty and openness. After all, Tim's question was not what I'd call "self-actualizing."

JOURNAL ENTRY — WEDNESDAY MORNING

This question reminds me of the Clint Eastwood movie, *In the Line of Fire*. The pivotal question in the movie was, If the situation ever presented itself, would Clint, a secret service agent, be willing to step into the line of fire and take a bullet for the President of the United States?

That's an easy one for me. I tend to be somewhat apolitical, and I haven't really been all that fond of any of the presidents that have held office in my lifetime. I had heard in my high school history classes that John Kennedy was a pretty cool guy, but all the stories about his womanizing made me wonder. Maybe old JFK was just out to take care of his sexual urges, while the country kind of ran itself. Still, we idolize him yet today, so maybe there *was* substance to his policies and programs. Wasn't he, after all, the guy that came up with the idea of the Peace Corps?

But die for him? Instead of him? I don't think so. Johnson? Nixon? Ford? Carter? Reagan? Bush? Clinton? Connie would be furious no matter which one of them I took a bullet for. (Geez, my old English teacher would hate *that* sentence.)

So who *would* I die for? Connie, I'm sure. I mean, if she was about to get hit by a car, I'd step in the way and try to save her. At least I think I would. Hard to know when it's actually about to happen. Despite our ups and downs I love her, though. No doubt about that.

And Josh and Amy? They're my kids and I love 'em. If they needed my liver or my kidney to live, I'd lie down on that operating table in a minute. Step in front of the same car that was about to hit Connie, too.

Who else? My parents? That's a tough one. They've had a good life...long and healthy and good. I have a lot of life ahead of me. Gotta think about that one some more. That *definitely* leaves Connie's elderly mother out of the picture here.

Bruce and John? Those butt-heads who got the promotions I should have, by kissing the right you-know-whats at the right time. Sorry guys, you're on your own.

I guess the bottom line is that whoever I died for would have to deserve it. They'd have to be my blood. They'd have to love me as much as I loved them. I'm not going to die for some worthless nobody. Or even some worthwhile person that I don't know — even if they're a John F. Kennedy on their way to saving the world.

My timing was great! I had just finished jotting down my last thought when the chime announcing lunch sounded. I looked at my watch and a big surprise hit me. I had missed lunch! The chime was for the afternoon seminar. I couldn't believe it!

Journal and pen in hand, I started down the hill and, without trying, caught up with "Bonnie of Hollywood." I admit I can't see the glow of plants and trees, but for some reason I can sure see it

The Spirit of Tocayo

in this woman. Her smile is warmer than a forest fire. And it's not a sexual thing either. I mean, I know she doesn't have the hots for me or anything, but her smile seems to draw me closer and make me sense that an intimate form of communication is taking place. It's as if — in the silence — she is bursting with things to say. And, somewhere deep inside me, I'm willing to listen. Pretty weird.

I settled down in my chair and wondered to myself if this was going to be another of Tim's "zip in, say a few choice words, zip out" seminars. I had expected to do more listening than writing as the days rolled on, but so far that hadn't been the case.

I don't know how he did it, but Tim again seemed to appear out of nowhere. Did he study under David Copperfield, or something? I opened my journal, ready to preserve his latest revelation for posterity.

"The story continues," were the first words out of Tim's mouth.

I knew which story he meant: the poor, destitute, broken son who returned to his wealthy father, hoping for nothing more than to become a humble servant. Great story. Wish I knew what it *really* meant.

"After the father welcomed the son back into his arms, he threw a terrific party. He called to his servants, '*Bring a clean set of clothes and dress him. Put the family ring on his finger...get a grain-fed heifer and roast it. We're going to feast! We're going to have a wonderful time! My son is here — given up for dead and now alive! Given up for lost, and now found. And they began to have a wonderful time.*'

"You see," Tim went on, "the point of this story is that the son believed that he deserved to be alienated from his father. He had blown it. He expected to spend the rest of his life as a farmhand in order to pay back the fortune that he had squandered partying and sowing his wild oats. But his father welcomed him, dressed him in new clothes, placed a valuable ring on his finger, and threw a party in his honor. His father put an end to the alienation the son felt he had coming to him.

"This is what I'm trying to explain to you about the God-Presence, as I lead you through these seminars. You may not even believe in the mystery of the God-Presence. You may reject the very thought that such an energy exists, based on your intellect, or past experience, or your deep-rooted doubt.

"But when the God-Presence welcomes you home, all of your misconceptions and apprehensions will be completely suspended — imprisoned is maybe a better word — within the limited confines of life as you know it now. You will question why you ever allowed doubts to overpower your mind. And you will be immediately transported into a new life — a never-ending life. You will be dressed in eternal clothing, the greatest treasure of all will be placed on your finger, and a party will be held in your honor in the celestine world.

"*The Message* says that when just one person — no matter what race, no matter what sex, no matter whether rich or poor or straight or gay, in any nation anywhere on this planet — recognizes and accepts the open, welcoming arms of the God-Presence, whatever they *were* becomes of less importance, and what they *can become* increases in importance. They are accepted, they are loved, and their self-centeredness is erased by the indisputable, irrevocable energy of sacrifice, reconciliation, and healing. Alienation is wiped away by a power so awesome that it cannot be quantified by science or mathematics, expressed by any known language, defined by religion or philosophy, or understood through emotion.

"It is beyond the heart and mind. It is beyond that elusive unknown we call the soul. It is a totally, completely inner experience. There is no substitute for that experience. It transcends description. It defies understanding.

"But I want to warn you about something. If you are someday able to partake in it, and you try to put it into words, you will be the object of scorn and ridicule. Those who have not yet reached this insight will call you a fool. You will ultimately realize that your purpose in life is to help others reach this insight. Money will diminish in its importance. Where you go and what you do will suddenly become meaningless. The people in your life will become your focus. Your relationships will be fulfilled because you are no longer alienated — no longer the center of a universe that has suddenly become larger."

Tim continued to talk and I continued to take notes. But I was beginning to tune out. This was more than I could handle — more than I wanted to handle.

I just wanted to be a husband who loved his wife and was loved in return. I wanted to be a father who cared for his children and was respected in return. I wanted to be a good person who deserved the admiration of a few close friends who understood what I was all about. And I wanted to be someone who made a difference in a world that was rapidly becoming too crowded, too polluted, too cruel, too greedy, and too crime-filled — an entirely too inhumane place to live.

Yet what Tim said was appealing. I was eager to believe that there was something beyond the life cycle. You know — get born, learn to walk and feed yourself, go to school, get a job, get married and have kids, acquire "stuff," go on a few vacations to wherever, get old and wrinkled and weak, spend a few years in a nursing home drooling all over your clothes and sheets, "go" everywhere but in the pot, die alone in the dark of the night, have a nice little gathering of your friends where they say great things about you, and rot in some box your family spent too much money on because you deserved it, poor slob.

The words and ideas of *The Celestine Prophecy* always seem to come back to me at times like this. I can't remember the Ninth Insight exactly, but I think it says that if we all vibrate at a high enough energy level, we'll follow the path of the ancient Mayans and of Jesus Christ, who all apparently ascended to another dimension because they figured out how to do it. If this vibrating stuff is left up to me, I've got this terrifying feeling I'm not going to make it into the next dimension. Geez, I can't even figure out how to make my marriage work!

The Next
Question

I managed to ignore the remainder of whatever it was Tim was saying until he dismissed us. Dinner was still over two hours away, so I decided to go back to my cabin. It was too nice to be inside, and my chair seemed to be starved for sunshine, so I dragged it outside, positioned it on the bare spot next to the steps, and sat down. Sure wish I could have seen the lake from this side of the cabin, but I was too lazy to haul my chair around to the other side, so this would just have to do.

"Forget Tim and his ethereal talk," I thought to myself. If only I could tune in public radio and listen to Mozart or Handel or Garrison Keillor or something. Could use a little Lake Wobegon. This place was starting to sound too much like "Lake Woe Be Unto You" to me.

"Well, by golly," I said aloud in my best Gomer Pyle accent, "I do believe I'll write in my li'l ol' journal."

Two or three steps into the cabin was all it took to grab it — had to save my energy for dinner, after all — and I was back in my chair to write.

JOURNAL ENTRY — WEDNESDAY AFTERNOON

All this talk about another life in another dimension has forced me to ask one huge question. If there is such a thing as eternity, would I really want to spend the whole entire thing with Connie? I still think I love her enough to stay married to her here and now. But forever? A big party in the sky with this God-Presence — whoever or whatever that is — and I'd have Connie at my side every minute?

I remember meeting her my last year in college. I thought she looked like one of the girls on *Charlie's Angels*, that TV show that had three gorgeous babes but no plot. (Oops, for a minute there I forgot I can't refer to women as "babes." Hey, I'm a "sensitive new-age guy," to quote the song.)

We got married, and both Connie and I quickly got engrossed in our careers. Then, as the result of a magical night at a Holiday Inn on our first anniversary, we brought Josh into the world. Things changed pretty quickly. Late night sex turned into early morning feedings. Those firm breasts I loved to play with developed a bit of a sag. Our second child, Amy, was accompanied by Connie's brand-new stretch marks.

Me being 100% heterosexual male, though, I still was interested in practicing those old "baby-making techniques." But Connie seemed to be less interested. She was pouring all of her attention into being the Mom-of-the-Century.

What was left for me? Well, I decided to be Dad-of-the-Decade. Hey, it was the best I could do. So, I was

Josh's hockey coach, Amy's soccer referee, a pretty darn good Cub Scout leader, and I had the best lawn on the entire block.

This all seemed to work for me until about two years ago, when we hired this new girl — or should I say "woman" — at work. Her name was Kim. She was twenty-four, married, with a two-year old daughter. I didn't give her much thought, except that I noticed she was beautiful. She kind of reminded me of Connie back when we met — dark hair, great tan, fit and trim. A "10," as we used to say.

As we got to know each other, I discovered two things. She was not just pretty, she was bright, witty, educated, with a great sense of humor. And she was not all that happily married — a fact she communicated to me at about the same time her glances seemed to linger and her smile seemed to become more infectious.

Well, I sure didn't need this! The message I picked up at home was "disinterested." The message I got from Kim was, "Hey, you, come here!"

At first, my strategies for ignoring her come-ons worked pretty well, even though I was flattered that she'd pick up on an "older man."

But then a funny — or, really, not so funny — thing started happening at home. We experienced a couple of financial reversals. My investment in my friend's startup software company went sour when he was sued by a big, greedy West Coast software giant. We had put just about everything we had into it. How could I misjudge such a sure thing? That was followed immediately by a major roof problem that caused a lot of interior damage in our house. *Thousands* of dollars worth.

Then, the biggie. Connie's dad died, and that about did her in. Sudden heart attack in his sleep. He never even knew what hit him. Connie and her father were really close, although I could never figure out why. He was your basic crabby old man, and he really didn't like me or even my kids — his own grandchildren.

Connie decided to quench her grief with counseling. Lots of expensive, time-consuming, away-from-home, no-dinner-for-Jeff counseling. My opinion is that it didn't work.

About that same time, I missed out on a major promotion at work I was counting on (and should have gotten), and Amy came down with life-threatening pneumonia and was hospitalized for eleven days.

To say things got kind of tense around our house would be a severe understatement. Connie started to take her anger out on me and the kids. Yelling, screaming, crying, locking herself in the bathroom. It was like some stupid "B" movie.

I felt like the odd man out. Sex was gone. Money was wasting away. Good times had vanished. We didn't see friends. And I was real sick of frozen pizza.

So, I decided it was time to take care of myself. I was way too young to turn in my sex drive for a front-wheel-drive Plymouth.

"So, Kim," I said one day, sounding a lot like a character from that same dorky movie, "do you have to hurry right home, or do you have time for a quick drink?"

I have a confession to make. In my entire life, I'd never asked that kind of question unless I was sure what the answer would be. And I was sure.

It was just an innocent drink. Only one each. We said something really dumb like, "We'll have to do this again sometime," and parted company.

I couldn't *wait* to do it again. A couple of days later, I approached her and asked her out. Only this time it turned out to be more than one drink. And it wasn't all that innocent. We absorbed ourselves in each other's eyes. I looked at her not as a co-worker but as a potential lover. I could picture myself in her arms. I knew it would be incredible!

She really made me feel important and special. No one has ever listened to me like she did. Or so readily appreciated me for who I am. And the look on her face — in her eyes and her smile — was more than just an "it's-fun-to-be-with-a-good-buddy" look. She was as ready for me as I was for her.

Drinks turned into dinner. Dinner turned into hugs in the parking lot. Hugs turned into kisses. Kisses turned into unbuttoned, unzipped clothes in my car. I was going crazy. She looked good, she kissed great, she felt wonderful. I had forgotten what a young woman felt like.

So much for dying for Connie. I probably could have died *because* of Connie. If she knew what I was up to while I was supposedly in a "client meeting," I'd be a statistic of domestic violence.

Fortunately, my incredible will power (or was it Kim's incredible will power?) took control before I managed to betray Connie completely. Still, in the back of my mind, I've occasionally regretted that we didn't "do it."

In the intervening months, I've thought that Connie may have suspected I was up to something. Maybe she could smell Kim's cologne on me. Maybe there was something about the way I walked or talked that gave me away. Maybe she could read my mind, kind of like I sometimes think Tim can read it.

The two themes at Tocayo Habitat appear to be "alienation" and "self-centeredness." My experiences, with my life at home and with Kim, were probably the perfect examples. I felt alienated from Connie, and my overt lust for Kim was probably the most self-centered form of self-centeredness anyone could imagine.

So, I'm not perfect after all.

Old Ways —
New Beginnings

Without even thinking about it or planning for it, I noticed an unexpected change in my eating habits at Tocayo. I was, indeed, caring less and less about "Three Squares a Day."

It was already after 5:00 P.M., and I had passed on all the day's meals. Even now, I wasn't really hungry. I had sipped on some water throughout the day, but I was so intent on taking notes and keeping up my journal that when the meal bells rang, I either missed them or ignored them, and spent the time thinking and writing instead.

I think the reason I wasn't hungry is that I was so absorbed with what was going on in my mind and in my heart that the needs of my body diminished by comparison.

Still, the thought of seeing those familiar faces across the table interested me. In fact, I actually felt a bit deprived, not having seen them at breakfast or lunch.

So when the dinner chime sounded, I zipped down that hill quicker than the chipmunks I had seen scurrying around the retreat grounds.

I was looking forward to a quiet, calming experience, drinking in the expressions on the faces of the others while enjoying yet another low-fat, low-cholesterol meal, so I found myself hoping that Tim wouldn't interrupt it with some provocative thought or activity. That hope was short-lived.

"I've got an optional assignment for you," Tim announced from the back of the dining room. "If you'd prefer to listen to music and 'zone out,' you don't have to do this."

It occurred to me that I should be one of the "zoners," until he explained further.

"What I'd like you to do is take a close look at the others at your table. Then I want you to consider the many positive qualities we can possess as human beings, and then I want you to think about which person or persons at your table best exemplify those characteristics. For starters, here are some of the qualities I look for in people: Compassion, Forgiveness, Wisdom, Understanding, Intuitiveness, Self-sacrifice, Affirmation, Stability, Loyalty, Discipline, and Humility. You can add to these, or take away from them, any way you see fit. Come up with your own list. But as you consider those attributes, I want you to view them in the context of a single word — Love. Are they words that describe what love is all about? Do you personally possess any of them? All of them? We'll be talking about some of these things in the days ahead, but it's not vital that you think about them now."

Well, after that introduction, I don't think anyone in the room could ignore the assignment. There we sat, chewing on our brussels sprouts, alternately staring at each other, wondering who had the most wisdom or compassion. Wondering which of us was the best example of forgiveness or self-sacrifice.

I looked around the table, locking in on the eyes of the others as I did. The doctor looked as though he possessed the qualities of wisdom, discipline, and stability. But maybe I just thought that because I believe doctors would need those attributes.

Our lonely homemaker, Mary Beth, was, in my judgment, a shining example of self-sacrifice, humility, and loyalty. But then, with *her* marriage, what other options would she have?

I decided there was something special about Bonnie-of-Hollywood. She probably had the most of everything, because she smiled a lot and seemed to be at peace with her life as it currently stood. There was a brief glimmer of reminiscent pain or hurt in her eyes, but that look was overwhelmed by one of compassion and forgiveness. This was probably just my imagination, too. I've never done this kind of thing before — how would I know what to look for? How would I know what I was seeing?

Until tonight, we hadn't had a seminar after dinner. But the thoughts and assignments seemed to be getting more intense, so Tim asked us all to gather in the meeting room when we were finished eating.

Usually, many in the group would linger over the last bite, listening to the remaining moments of the music, then slowly leave for their next destination — the meditation room, their cabins, or a walk by the lake in the evening sun. Tonight was different. We all skipped our last bites and took the short walk to the meeting room. To a bystander — had there been any nearby — it would have looked like a parade.

Before we had even settled into our chairs, Tim stepped up to the podium. "For the past few days, you've been spending your time defining love — describing its attributes. You've written your thoughts in your journals. Who would you be willing to die for? What price would you pay to express your love? How do you

deal with the hurts of the past? How do you end the alienation
you may be feeling?

"At dinner tonight, I asked you to look closely at the others
seated at your table. I suggested that you consider a number of
positive personal attributes that each of us can possess, and
determine if you could sense those attributes in one another. I
mentioned Compassion, Forgiveness, Wisdom, Understanding,
Intuitiveness, Self-sacrifice, Affirmation, Stability, Loyalty,
Discipline, and Humility. I'm sure you considered many more.
But no matter what you added or subtracted from the original list,
what you eventually came up with described the highest ideal we
can know: Love.

"And Love, I believe, is the ultimate, true, defining
characteristic of the God-Presence. We can't really know love until
we know the power who created love. We can't really experience
love until we experience the God-Presence in our lives.

"Listen to what the ancient manuscript says about the qualities
of love:

'I was hungry and you fed me,
I was thirsty and you gave me a drink,
I was homeless and you gave me a room,
I was shivering and you gave me clothes,
I was sick and you stopped to visit,
I was in prison and you came to me.'

"That's how I would define compassion, wouldn't you?
Now listen to this insight:

'Be wary of the shrewd advice that tells you how
to get ahead in the world on your own.
Giving, not getting, is the way.
Generosity begets generosity.

Stinginess impoverishes.'

"Isn't this the most compelling definition of self-sacrifice you've ever heard? Then there's this insight on humility:

'Don't push your way to the front;
don't sweet-talk your way to the top.
Put yourself aside, and help others get ahead.
Don't be obsessed with getting your own advantage.
Forget yourselves long enough to lend a helping hand.'

"*The Message* teaches that to achieve true greatness, we must be willing to be a servant. Here's what it says:

'Do you want to stand out? Then step down.
Be a servant.
If you puff yourself up, then you'll get the wind
knocked out of you.
But if you're content to simply be yourself,
your life will count for plenty.'

"How about the virtue of forgiveness? Listen:

'Be even-tempered, content with second place, quick to forgive an
offense...quickly and completely.'

"Simple instructions, yet so difficult to follow.

"Regarding affirmation and loyalty, *The Message* says,

'Laugh with your happy friends when they're happy;
share tears when they're down.
Get along with each other; don't be stuck up.
Make friends with nobodies; don't be the great somebody.' "

Tim closed the book and looked around the room, gauging our many and varied reactions.

"If you've listened carefully and honestly, you may have come to this conclusion. These teachings from *The Message* run contrary to what we currently believe in our society. They are the exact opposite. These ideals seem to more accurately reflect the counterculture of the late sixties and early seventies. Many of us idolized the revolution of free love and experimentation with drugs, which we now know to be the negative expressions of that counterculture. But in the midst of it all, the people of that time exhibited caring attitudes toward other human beings. We cared about equality. We marched with Martin Luther King. We abhorred violence and war. We joined the Peace Corps and served the basic needs of people in far-off places. Now, years later, we seem to have turned our backs on these ideals.

"Oh, sure, we want peace in the world. We walk ten kilometers for the disease of our choice. We give to the United Way, and we donate canned goods to the local food shelves.

"But if we're really honest with ourselves, we only give to the limits of our comfort zones. We don't see love as sacrifice. Even in our marriages, we only want what's good for *us*. So *The Message* reveals to us the true counterculture — the spiritual dimension we had all hoped to discover."

About this time, I wanted to — for probably the tenth time since I'd arrived at Tocayo — stand up and shout, "OH, SHUT UP, TIM. I'm here to figure out who I AM, not who you or your 'message' think I OUGHT to be!" Why didn't this guy get the picture of why we were all there?

Tim continued, oblivious to the doubt that flooded my mind. "You all have met Michael. Michael has been a part of our family at Tocayo for about two years now. Back then, I wouldn't have asked him to do what he's going to do now. A year ago, I still wouldn't have asked. Even six months ago, he may not have been ready."

In unison, we all shifted our eyes from Tim and glanced

around the room, looking for Michael, pausing to ask each other with our questioning expressions just what was going on.

"Michael is going to share his spiritual journey with us," Tim said.

"Oh, oh, here we go," I thought. "I've heard this kind of stuff before, I'm sure. Male subject grows up in small town, goes to college in the big city, experiments with drugs, protests war-of-the-day, meets girl, falls in love, gets married, has kids, troubles come, gets divorced, becomes alcoholic, finds God on street corner, life turned around in an instant. This is supposed to be 'everyman's' story, and because it is, I'm supposed to identify with it."

We all watched as Michael walked slowly to the front of the room, hesitation in every move. He stepped behind the podium, looked down for a few moments, then looked up at his audience.

Nice dramatic touches, don't you think?

He began to speak, and from that moment on, I was in his spell.

"Twenty-two years ago, before some of you were born, while some of you were still in grade school, I killed a young mother of a seven-year-old kid. She didn't deserve to die. She had done nothing wrong to me. Nothing to hurt me.

"I needed money, and they lived in this expensive house in this big-money neighborhood. The lights were out and it was kind of early at night, and I didn't know their husband and daddy was out of town on business. So I let myself in through a window by busting out the glass. I was looking through their stuff trying to find the things I could sell for the most money when she must've heard me.

"She came down the stairs in her night gown, and she was

scared. I could tell. She said, 'Who's there?' and I stepped into the dark alongside the stairway. When she got down far enough on the steps, I lit into her with my knife. I cut hard and deep. The more she struggled and screamed, the harder I attacked her. I heard her kid crying, and I looked up to the top of the stairs. There she was watching me cut into her mother. My first thought was, 'I have to kill her, too,' but something inside me told me to run, so I did.

"I didn't know what to do or where to go, so I drove to a gas station and went into the men's room. I looked in the mirror and couldn't believe what I saw. I was covered with her blood. I made sure the door was locked, and I started to wash. I washed my hands and face. I took off my jacket and jeans and started washing the blood out of them. Some of it didn't want to come out.

"I heard a knock on the door. I was afraid to answer. The knocking turned to pounding. 'You all right in there?' a voice said. It must have been the station attendant. I didn't know what to do. My jeans were in the sink, soaking wet, so I couldn't open the door. The knocking and pounding didn't let up.

"Then it was quiet, except for the muffled sound of cars coming and going, getting gas. I kept washing. Her blood stuck to me like glue.

"Suddenly, without any warning, the restroom door flew open, and there stood the station manager and two cops. One cop looked at me and drew his gun. I backed into the corner and put my hands into the air. I knew I couldn't run. It was over. I was finished."

Michael paused and wiped the sweat from his forehead. I had never heard such quiet in a room filled with people. No one moved. No one coughed. I'm not even sure anyone was breathing.

My first impulse was to get up and leave. I didn't want to hear more, although I was sure the worst was over. How could I be in the same place as a cold-blooded murderer? How could Tim have him here as a part of Tocayo? This was supposed to be a spiritual retreat, not a haven for slashers. This made no sense.

Michael began to speak again.

"My trial was short. The woman's daughter picked me out of a police lineup. The blood on my clothes matched her mother's blood. My old car had been spotted in the neighborhood. The evidence all pointed to me. Finally, with guilt and remorse overwhelming me, I confessed.

"I was sentenced to twenty-six years for second-degree murder and burglary and about four other things. I was transferred from the county jail to the state prison, stripped of my few possessions. I never heard what happened to my apartment and my stuff in it. But it really didn't matter.

"Prison life was hell, but then, I deserved hell, so I was in the right place. My first priority was to live. To survive. Because in the prison system, if you're weak, you're dog meat for the other prisoners. I didn't deliberately want to get into fights, but sometimes they couldn't be avoided. I stuck a fork in a guy's gut once, and that landed me in solitary. But I got respect, and after that, people pretty much left me alone.

"Early on, the prison chaplain paid me visits. They always zero in on the new guys. I guess they figure they're more vulnerable. But this guy had nothing to say that interested me. 'God loves you,' he said. 'Oh, sure,' I said.

"I decided to finish my high school diploma in prison and learn as much as I could. My goal was to shape up and maybe get some time off for good behavior. I figured I could sure do that without God.

"Still, good behavior or not, I knew inside that I deserved worse than they could ever dish out. I knew I really deserved to die for what I'd done. That almost would have been easier. That way it would have been over. I'd be done with the guilt. The guilt was eating away at me. And I lived with it for years. Every day...every night. The nights were the longest."

As Michael continued his story, my mind turned to one of the many debates raging in this country — the one over the death penalty. If it's not considered for football stars or the children of the wealthy, why do the poor and the uneducated face it so often? I've never even understood the difference between first-and second-and third-degree murder. If you're the victim, you're dead. And if you did it, you're the murderer. There are no degrees of death. Why are there degrees of guilt?

I'm not saying I'm in favor of the death penalty. I mean, I'm a pretty liberal guy. But as Michael related all these terrible details, I almost wanted to throw the switch myself. How could this guy stand up here and tell us about it like nothing had happened? What about that child? Michael had destroyed her life. Didn't *that* bother him?

I imagine I had missed a lot of Michael's story before I finally tuned in again.

"One day when I was feeling pretty sorry for myself," Michael was saying, " a guard came to my cell and asked me if I wanted a visitor. He said it was a guy named 'Brother Duane.' I said I didn't know any Brother Duane, but my days were awfully lonely, so I went to the visiting room.

"Brother Duane looked like he had arrived at the gate on a Harley chopper. Scraggly hair, scruffy beard, black leather jacket with a couple of rips in it. Black boots. I didn't even know guys like this still existed in the nineties. The last one I saw was twenty years ago or so, before I got put away. So I never thought they'd be around when I was getting close to parole.

"I asked Brother Duane, 'What do you want with me?' He said, 'I'm here to show you the way to freedom. I'm here to help you wipe your record clean.'

"'Who sent you here?' I asked him. 'How do you know about me?'

"He had a worn, tired look on his face. But something about him radiated an energy — an energy I could only describe as love. His answer blew me away. 'I was sent by the real victim of your crime — by the daughter of the one whose life you took.'

"I wanted to spit in his face through the opening in the glass and walk away. What kind of cruel joke was he playing? Was this guy really an angel from hell? Was he here to torment me?

"He continued, 'She sent me here to tell you that you don't have to live in guilt and remorse the rest of your life. She called on me because I have pointed many men — many of your fellow prisoners — to the freedom that comes from the God-Presence. Freedom that can be yours. She wants you to know this freedom.'

" 'Why?' I asked. 'Why would she care? Why would anyone care? What does she want from me?'

" 'She wants nothing from you except that you find what she's found. Peace from the memories that have tormented her. Memories of that night, and of you. She wants you to find that peace.' "

Man, this guy was good! I looked around and there wasn't a dry eye in the house. The normally unemotional doctor held his head in his hands and stared at the floor. Mary Beth had tears in her eyes. Bonnie-of-Hollywood was actually sobbing. I have to admit, this was even getting to me.

"That day, in that prison visiting room," Michael continued, "I discovered that each of us can have two lives — the life we had before we understand and accept the gift of the God-Presence, and the life we have after the God-Presence illuminates our inner being. Brother Duane helped me understand that *The Message* teaches that the God-Presence gives us a fresh start. The old ways are gone forever, and everything becomes new. *Everything.* We not only settle our relationship with the God-Presence, but, as a result, we are then able to settle our relationships with each other. It's like when the ground that's been frozen by the winter thaws in the spring, and new life comes out of the soil. And the wind blows the seeds and the pollen, and the colors bloom everywhere. That's the only way I can describe what happened to me that day. And I'm glad I can tell you about it. *The Message* instructs me that I have the task of telling everyone what the God-Presence has done and is doing and can do. That's why I'm here. That's my spiritual journey."

Michael stepped down and walked to the back of the room. I didn't know what to think. I hoped he was the only killer in the room. Actually, I had no idea there would be *any* killers at Tocayo. About the only crimes I could identify with were of the white-collar variety. The kind where some little old widow entrusted her life savings to an "investment counselor," and he or she skipped off with the bucks to some island off the coast of New Zealand. Every time I read about that sort of thing in the newspaper, I get boiling mad. That actually happened to an aunt of mine about three years ago. She was left with nothing. I hope I never run into the jerk. I'd probably end up in prison having conversations with

"Brother Duane."

The room was still very quiet when Tim replaced Michael at the podium. This guy must live in khaki slacks and denim shirts. I was beginning to wonder if there was anything else in his wardrobe.

"Michael has just shared his life experiences — in a way, his spiritual journey. His search took an unconventional path and occurred in an unlikely place — behind the concrete walls and steel bars of a prison.

"I know it was hard for Michael to share all of this. And I know it was hard for you to listen. I saw mixed feelings of compassion and anger and fear on your faces as he was speaking.

"You undoubtedly noticed that Michael's journey didn't involve a rock formation or an energy vortex, or a trip to a lost city or retreat, or prayer and meditation. It's a simple story. He just needed the things that the God-Presence offered to him.

"Your personal journey is likely different, and it is as individual as you are. Remember, on our first day here, I said that no two people travel exactly the same path. Your experiences and insights are as valid as Michael's or mine, because they happened to you.

"I know it's late and you probably want to go back to your cabins and spend some quiet time and sleep. But I do have an assignment for you. I want you to chart your personal spiritual pilgrimage to date. Write all your thoughts in your journal. You can begin tonight, or tomorrow. You can finish it here at the Habitat, or you can continue working on it for a lifetime. Remember, no one is comparing your journey to that of others, or measuring your progress. You are not engaged in a competition. You are creating a unique road map of your personal experiences.

"Think about your early yearnings for spiritual reality, and specifically your more recent spiritual awakening and insights. What are the fruits of these experiences? Where have they taken you? Where are you spiritually going?

"In the days that remain, you can share all of your thoughts, some of your thoughts, or none of your thoughts with me in our conferences. You're not doing this for me. You're doing it for yourself."

Tim said good night, met Michael in the back of the room, and they walked out together. Nearly everyone else followed on their heels. A few of us stayed behind — me, the guy from the lakeside cabin who almost always beats me to the shower, Bonnie-of-Hollywood, and four or five others I had only noticed in passing. I could tell we all had things on our minds.

I sat there and pondered my pilgrimage and my days here so far. Was this taking me *anywhere*? Had I come anywhere over the past two years on my lonely, frustrating search for spiritual reality?

For some strange reason, I looked forward to putting my thoughts and experiences in chronological order. I thought that would help me discover if there was any purpose and direction behind it all.

The room continued to slowly empty out. Before long, I was the last one in the room. I decided that my bed, saggy as it was, would provide better sleeping accommodations than the chair, so I headed for my cabin.

I had every intention of writing in my journal, but I must have fallen asleep before my head hit the pillow. The next thing I knew, it was morning.

Stepping Out of My Comfort Zone

I couldn't believe how early I awakened. The last time I remembered getting up at that time of the morning, I was in my first year of college. I was too new to realize that nobody showed up for Psychology 101 at 6:50 in the morning. That class was so huge it was held in the auditorium, and with nearly 4,000 students, it was more than twice the size of my hometown. I figured out once that they could have fit roughly 62.5 of my high school graduating classes in that single room.

To pass Basic Psych, all we had to do was study the notes and keep up with the reading assignments.

Now here I was at Tocayo — about as far from the logic and discipline of a college education as I could get. The sunrise was hours away, and all I could think about was creating this so-called "road map" of my spiritual journey.

I turned on the light, propped my pillow up against the headboard, opened my journal, and stared at the blank pages. This was a tough one. My spiritual journey was more frustration than insight. Every time I thought I was on the verge of making a great discovery, I stumbled onto more questions. Finally, I decided that the best place to begin was the beginning — as best I could remember it.

JOURNAL ENTRY — THURSDAY MORNING — MY PILGRIMAGE

As a child, I remember being taught to pray. Mom believed in God, and she taught me infantile little prayers like "Now I lay me down to sleep, I pray the Lord my soul to keep, etc.," and that famous prayer before meals, "Come Lord Jesus, be our guest, let this food to us be blessed." Well, at least they rhymed, so they were easy to remember.

Dad went along to church, but I don't think his heart was in it. His favorite prayer at meals was "Good Bread, Good Meat, Good Lord, Let's Eat!" Mom, I determined later, didn't think that was all that funny.

I guess during those early years there was no question that I believed there was a God — of course I had even more belief and enthusiasm for Santa Claus, the Easter Bunny, and the Tooth Fairy. At least they brought goodies — presents, chocolate eggs, and quarters. In my mind, all that was a bit more believable than an invisible "God."

Somewhere toward the end of my years of middle school, Dad had his big "experience with God." He "found Jesus." I can't say as I understood much about it, but our family began to attend church more frequently and they shoved me into Sunday school. Geez, was *that* boring!

All of this did affect me, though. I remember thinking a lot about God — even praying seriously. But mostly that "serious prayer" had to do with things I needed or wanted. I'd pray that God would help me get that cool bike I lusted after for Christmas. It didn't actually work all the time, but it was better than Santa, the bunny, and the fairy — all of whom had been totally destroyed by my schoolmates. They had figured out the big lies before I had.

I remember there was this time I desperately wanted my soccer coach to pick me as a goalie. I prayed hard, he picked another guy, and I got pretty upset with the whole idea of God.

Throughout those years, there were times I had serious thoughts about God. I went to summer church camp one year, mostly because this cool blond named Annette went. She was a year ahead of me in school, but I thought I was up to *that* simple challenge.

Despite the distraction of Annette, who for the most part ignored me, I still experienced an intense desire to know God. Was he real, did he offer the peace I wanted? Did he really care about me? Could he cure my zits?

My high school years were painful for me. But I guess they were for a lot of kids — and still are for the kids today. I found it wasn't cool to talk about God. It sure wasn't "in" to be known as one who went to church. I suppose that is when I first heard people seriously questioning the faith that I had been trying so hard to accept for myself.

I discovered that the church leaders I had admired

so much weren't able to answer the questions I was learning to ask. They didn't seem to even speak the same language. We were told what to believe. We were told what it would take to please God. My questions were unacceptable to my parents. Every question had some stupid "canned" answer they found in a Bible verse — my folks just didn't connect. I longed for the day when I would be free to express no faith at all. I wanted to find my own answers.

Of course, when I got free of my parents' control, I looked to sex and rebellion and Colt 45 malt liquor and "handmade cigarettes" for my answer. (At least I didn't inhale!) Sadly, I experienced feelings of guilt about all this. I didn't know if this guilt resulted from my mother's warnings about promiscuity and drugs, or from the things I had been taught by my Sunday school teachers, or from something deeper inside me.

Still, I took a part of that "old-time religion" to college with me. I had these suspicions that Christianity couldn't possibly stand up to the knowledge we had gained in the fields of biology and sociology. And it certainly couldn't "pass muster" under the scrutiny of my more thoughtful, educated friends.

So I checked out of the religion scene. It wasn't that I was angry with those who had spiritual convictions. Perhaps in keeping with the times, the only people who angered me were those who were intolerant — those who had all of the answers, even when they weren't interested in listening to my questions. I became convinced that if there was a God, he was not any more interested in me than I was in him.

After graduation, I focused on getting married to the "right girl." I wanted to start a family and build close relationships with others who thought and felt the way I did and shared the same concerns — the environment, overpopulation, nuclear proliferation, and racism. These thoughts consumed much of my time in college. I decided the purpose of my existence was to build a better life for myself, for those I loved, and for a world that didn't have the sense or vision to do that for itself.

About that time, I started getting serious with Connie, and it looked like everything was coming together. We got married about five months after graduation.

My thoughts were disrupted by the breakfast chime. I had no idea I had been so totally absorbed in my writing. I hadn't even taken a shower.

I splashed on some cologne and put on a fresh shirt, hoping the combination would mask my oversight.

It would have been relatively easy for me to skip breakfast again today — I wasn't all that hungry. But I thought it would be fun to study the others at my table. For all I knew, some of them may have departed Tocayo, fearful that Michael might turn on them without warning. "This could be interesting," I said silently as I followed the path down to the lodge.

I was the first to be seated at my table. Maybe they all did skip out on the rest of the week. I looked toward the back of the room to see if I could spot the arrival of the others from my group. Sure enough, they straggled in. All except Bonnie. Most of them looked fairly tired.

Breakfast was "same old, same old." I probably won't eat another banana for years. At least they had plum jam this particular morning. What a refreshing change.

Tim did his usual conversation with "God-Presence" but threw in a twist and suggested that we all face the tasks of the day with honesty and openness. Then he announced that, although we would still have our private conferences throughout the day, our morning seminar was canceled. "You probably need time to meditate and write," he said.

Actually, he was right. I couldn't wait to get back to my journal. I finished my last sip of orange juice and headed toward the door. As I walked toward the exit, I noticed Bonnie and Michael engrossed in conversation. "Why is *she* allowed to talk?" I wondered. "Doesn't she have to observe the same rule of silence as the rest of us?" Then it occurred to me that she was probably scheduling her conference with Tim. Changing her time maybe.

The weather was too nice to consider confining myself to my cabin, so I found myself walking to a wooded knoll that overlooked the east end of the lake. The sun was warm, there was a gentle breeze, and as I sat in the shade of a large but apparently dying tree, I felt myself at peace. Peace with the world around me — peace with the world within — a wonderful place to examine the paths I had taken in my spiritual travels since college.

JOURNAL ENTRY — THURSDAY MORNING, CONTINUED...

Marriage was not the bump-free, breakdown-free road I had anticipated. Things went sour more than once. Initially, Connie and I had our difficulties adjusting to each other. I was still in the old college party mode, and she had her sights set on a comfortable suburban life. Eventually, I bought into her goals, and we found ourselves in hot pursuit of financial stability.

That stability evaded us — in fact, a couple of times we found ourselves on the verge of bankruptcy, and the fights became more frequent. The uncertainty of not being able to provide for my wife and children caused unbelievable stress. The straightforward task of meeting the needs of the family appeared to have come so easily to my parents; I couldn't understand why it wasn't working for me. My parents were nearing retirement and were pretty well set financially. Had the "land of opportunity" changed that much since I was a child?

We lost our first house due to my first extended experience with unemployment. When I found the job with the company I'm at now, we began saving and were finally able to make a down payment on a second house — partly because my father gave us some additional money. My goal was financial stability — but was that enough to take me through the disappointments in myself and in my ability to provide for my family? There had to be a purpose.

After we got back on our feet, I made a few really lousy investments. Connie was totally opposed to them, but I was sure we'd make a killing. Computers and software companies were really getting to be hot commodities.

In the course of meeting with my accountant to discuss plans for rescuing my family from the brink of disaster, we began to talk about spiritual experiences.

For years now, Duncan (I called him "Dunk" or "The Dunker") was the one guy I truly envied. He had an incredible knack for choosing the right mutual funds and picking only those stocks that went up even in a bear market. I would have loved to possess his expertise, or his luck, or whatever it was!

This particular day, though, he seemed like a different Dunk. He was very open and honest with me, and shared how he had become disillusioned with working the odds to build up a bigger nest egg. I wondered if he had just blown some big bucks and that was the reason for his new perspective.

"It just wasn't worth it," he shared. "It wasn't a good enough reason for being on this planet. My heart longed for something that brought genuine satisfaction."

I had a hard time relating to him until I saw that he truly meant what he said. His desire to connect into spiritual things was real — more real than I had ever seen in my folks. My dad had wanted the same things I wanted. It was just that he prayed about them, while I tried to make them a reality through hard work and investments. His desires were the same as mine — get ahead, achieve financial stability for the family, assure a good future for the kids. But his goals were made during the sixties when the economy was more favorable to those kind of prayers.

I could sense that Dunk had somehow realigned his

priorities. He was different. His life had been changed and his goals were completely outside himself — he wanted to connect with the spiritual powers around us and find significance in a world that was spiritual as well as physical. What he was talking about was out of my league at the time, but I was fascinated by his discoveries. It was the start of something very significant for me because I began to awaken out of a deep spiritual sleep.

Dunk loaned me his copy of *The Celestine Prophecy*. It was heavily marked — the pages were almost completely yellow from those highlighting pens.

I turned the pages eagerly and suddenly came across the first insight — there was purpose in what I was going through! A relief spread through me. Hope at last!

As I look back now, I could see that I had come to a point of despair. I had gone through so many unhappy and unfair experiences — something within me had said there had to be a reason for it all. "If there was no reason, and no greater purpose, then I was truly in trouble," I thought. "Maybe I should just end it all now instead of waiting for the scenario to play out."

Suddenly seeing that there may indeed be a spiritual world, I could search for purpose. I had been skeptical up to that point. I had been like so many of my friends, critical of others who held to spiritual values. My world began to open up to the fact that there was a spiritual realm — I had been living only aware of half of the reality that was around me.

There was just enough time before lunch to remove the stubble on my face and take a quick shower. I dropped my journal at my cabin and headed for the showers. The lunch chime was ringing as I walked toward the cabin, hair still wet, to put away my shaving kit and pick up my book.

The doctor noticed my wet hair as I took my place at the table, and a "what-kind-of-crazy-schedule-are-you-on-anyway?" look appeared on his face. At least I *think* that's what his expression was conveying.

I wasn't in the mood for any silly assignments at the table today, and, thankfully, Tim didn't give us any. I was actually more interested in getting back to my journal than anything else, though I did need the break — and the food. Vegetable pizza today. I was giving some thought to joining George Bush's "I Hate Broccoli Club" after the retreat was over.

If you can imagine such a thing as a hush coming over a room in which nobody was talking in the first place, that's what happened when Michael walked in and sat down by Tim. It was like everyone in the room was thinking the same thing: "So, Michael, kill anyone this morning?" Yet, I knew that was a ridiculous thought, and I'm sure everyone else felt the same way. Michael gave off the aura of a truly gentle, caring person. The old Michael must be gone forever. Like a snake, he must have shed his "old skin" in some dark prison cell.

I gulped down my meal, finished off a glass of water, and glanced at the place on my wrist where my watch would have been — had I remembered to put it on after my shower. Fortunately, the congresswoman was wearing a watch with a big enough face for me to see. It was ten after one; nearly two hours until my conference with Tim.

I went out to one of the chairs placed at strategic, private distances from each other on the lush green lawn surrounding the lodge...and made a note of some of the questions I wanted to ask Tim. Then I began to write, picking up where I had left off. More or less.

JOURNAL ENTRY — THURSDAY AFTERNOON

So now I've arrived at the big moment. Where have I come spiritually in the past year? Or, for that matter, in my entire life? What has led me to Tocayo Habitat, and what have I discovered along the way — if anything?

I remember the excitement I felt after reading *The Celestine Prophecy*. It was like I had been "born again." My folks talked about that experience, but their definition was so limited. It was strictly based on what was taught at the narrow-minded church we attended.

But the books I've read and the places I've gone have helped me to see manifestations of spiritual life all around me that I had ignored. Naturally, I wanted to learn more. I was sure there were greater insights on the horizon, just beyond my view.

One day, while reading through one of the many magazines that seem to magically reproduce themselves in our family room, I stumbled across a small classified that said "Indigenous American Tours — The Spirituality of our Hemisphere." I called the toll-free 800 number and a few weeks later, I received a cheap-looking black-and-white brochure that described various trips to the Amazon, Hidden Rain Forests, Peru, Mexico, and Navajo religious sites.

I couldn't believe this kind of thing actually existed. How long had these trips been available? How could I have missed out on these exotic experiences?

Eight weeks later, my ticket in hand, I was headed across the border on American Airlines. Connie wasn't all that excited about my "Vacation for One," as she called it, but I had new territory to cover. As I walked through the unfamiliar airport terminal in Mexico City and stood in line at the immigration desk, it occurred to me that I had stepped way out of my comfort zone. The reason must be that I was beginning to awaken to the spiritual person within me. I was hungry and thirsty for truth. I wanted to somehow get in touch with the people and cultures that had experienced the spiritual realities that were so foreign to me — no pun intended.

The immigration officer took my tourist card and passport, smiled, and then stamped each liberally. "What on earth would bureaucrats do without rubber stamps?" I wondered.

When I got to the baggage claim area, I noticed that all the signs were clearly printed in English as well as Spanish. What a relief! I had tried to brush up on the college courses I had taken in Spanish, but about all I could remember at that point was "Buenos dias." I grabbed my bags off the conveyer belt and shuffled along with everyone else toward customs. I was waved through quickly, and I stepped outside into the bright, hot Mexican sun.

The sight of hundreds — maybe even thousands — of people milling around waiting for taxis and busses startled me. As busy as Los Angeles International is, it still seemed uncrowded by comparison. I felt like the typical confused "gringo," until I saw a tall man with Native American features standing nearby, holding a sign that said "Indigenous Tours." I knew that sign was for me.

A few minutes later, I was crammed into a hot, stuffy micro-van with nine other members of the tour group, my luggage in my lap. Obviously, we all needed lessons on traveling light. We smiled at each other nervously. I wondered why they also chose a tour that promised discovery of the spiritual roots of our hemisphere. In a way, I felt like a gay man "coming out of the closet." I wasn't used to talking about spiritual things and had this sudden fear that I had parked my logic along with my brain somewhere back home. Still, I was excited — it was refreshing to do something so out of character.

We were driven to the Hotel Majestic. I'm sure it had been majestic quite a few decades ago, but it was *far* from glamorous now. The brochure said that it was strategically located, and the brochure was right. I could look out my window across the plaza and see the huge presidential palace.

We had dinner on the dining room balcony and had a beautiful view of the nearby cathedral. I truly love Mexican food, and this was a real treat! The chef must have invented some new varieties of hot peppers especially for this occasion!

That night I found it difficult to sleep. There were street noises, bells chiming at weird intervals from the cathedral, and no air-conditioning sounds to block them out. I woke up twice during the night, hyperventilating from the thin atmosphere. I'm sure the peppers didn't help, either.

Finally, I fell into a deep sleep. But not for long. My rest came to an abrupt and unwelcome end at 6:00 A.M., when the most god-awful trumpet music startled me. I flew out of bed, my heart pounding! I thought for sure it was a revolution! The government had fallen along with the peso!

As it turned out, it was simply a contingent of the Mexican army — out on the plaza to raise an enormous Mexican flag. The trumpeters needed more practice (*much* more), and the noise was deafening. So much for strategic locations. Despite the rude wake-up call, I was excited about the day.

After breakfast, we gathered in the lobby to meet our tour guide, Manuel. Our destination for the first day was Teotihuacán, "The City of the Gods."

Manuel told us that Teotihuacán is one of the "stars" of the more than 14,000 archeological sites scattered throughout Mexico. As we began the drive, he related the few facts that are known about the origins of the huge city complex which, to this day, has only partially been uncovered.

Some thirty miles outside of the city, we caught our first glimpse of two pyramids rising above the plateau. I tried to imagine how they would have appeared some two thousand years ago. They were built by people who had come to appreciate their spiritual roots. These people had developed to the point where they could live far above the "survival level" of their ancestors. They could afford to build magnificent buildings to commemorate their spiritual beliefs, and they could support a priestly caste. The priests could seek connections with the spiritual powers and lead the rest of the race in their spiritual discoveries.

Their priorities and realities had sure been different from mine! They weren't just looking for financial stability and a secure retirement. Everything they produced in excess of what they needed to sustain life was turned over to the priests to build these massive buildings so that they could express contact with their spiritual discoveries. I felt at that moment that their priorities somehow had to become my own.

The driver pulled up to a small archeological site outside of the main compound. This house supposedly had been used by the priestly architects of that incredible city. We walked through three rooms where we saw the remains of fresco paintings, their colors surprisingly bright even after nine hundred years. Manuel pointed to the various figures that represented the gods and spirits that had been worshipped in this place. I could tell that these people were truly in touch with the spiritual forces that ruled over the land and its inhabitants.

The god Tlaloc, still worshipped by those who

practice the ancient religions, was a prominent figure in the paintings. I felt strangely "in tune" with a culture that had so much history in comparison with my own. Theirs was a spiritual heritage that had many more answers about an integrated approach to understanding life. As I stood in there, I began to rethink everything I had been taught — and believed. I wondered what my parents would say.

We reboarded the van, went through the gates into the main archeological park, and were dropped off on the south side of the Pyramid of the Moon. As we walked through a field of scrub and brush toward the Pyramid of the Sun, we came on a small army of people selling trinkets and pottery. I ignored them. I was here to experience Teotihuacán, not bring back stuff that would end up in our next garage sale.

The sun and moon had long been the common denominators of "primitive" cultures. Manuel explained how the Meso-American cultures came to focus their worship on the forces that controlled nature.

We stopped for a few moments to meditate before beginning our ascent of the huge Pyramid of the Sun. The meditation experience seemed emptier than I had expected, maybe because it was so new and different to me. Yet I had an awesome sense of the centuries of deep worship that had taken place on this very site.

The others in our group must have better understood what it took to meditate — they appeared to be getting something out of it. Although I was a lightweight in these things, I still wanted to learn.

We sat on the steps leading up to a small platform, and I wondered to myself if there was any significance to the fact that there were thirteen steps. We faced the sun, which was now just rising over the top of the pyramid, and waited for the warmth to cover our bodies. A woman sitting next to me whispered that she sensed the spiritual energy of this place. I tried, of course, and thought I felt *something*. I don't know if it was spiritual energy, but I was excited. After about twenty minutes, we began to climb up the main steps on the front of the pyramid.

This thing was huge! Manuel told us that it was larger than any of the pyramids of Egypt. The concept behind these pyramids was completely different, too. Archeologists had spent time digging into the their cores but had found no secret passages. The pyramids had instead been platforms to raise men and women above the surface of the earth.

Small temples had been built atop the towering heights — places where intense spiritual energies and powers were concentrated. Though they existed in a now-distant time, these people had discovered a profound spiritual presence. I had been transported to a place and time a million miles and a thousand years away from the office. A long way, too, from the pressures to perform as a responsible twentieth-century husband and father.

I was out of breath by the time I got up to the third tier. So much for stair-climbing machines at the health club. Manuel was used to the high altitude, and was already quickly walking up the last flight of stairs.

A few minutes later I made it to the top, and, frankly, I was disappointed. This great pyramid was little more than a mound of rock. The small temple had long since eroded away. Something so sacred should last forever, I thought.

But I have to say, the view was breathtaking. We looked out over the beautiful countryside and the ruins of a city that had been lost for centuries. We sat there for more than two hours. Manuel and some of the others spent that time meditating. I guess I spent most of the time thinking and reflecting on how empty my existence had been. But at least I was finally doing something that was important to me, and I was strangely at peace.

My peaceful thoughts vanished when I remembered what little I knew about the history of this culture. Things had really turned sour. In their effort to appease the spirit world, the priests eventually began to sacrifice human beings. Virgins probably. Amy's age, maybe.

I forced these sickening thoughts out of my mind, and the peace I had felt eventually returned. I'm not sure I was experiencing a spiritual revolution, but I had sure been awakened to a new world of reality.

The Sum of the Parts

A dark shadow drifted across my pages as I wrote. At first, I thought it was a cloud obscuring the sun, but the edges of the shadow were too well defined.

I looked up. It was Tim. Oops! Looks like I accidentally blew off another conference.

"When you didn't show up, I remembered seeing you heading over here after lunch, so I thought I'd track you down," Tim said.

"Sorry," I mumbled.

"If it's okay with you, let's just meet out here," he added. "My office is kind of stuffy, and it's a great day."

"Fine with me."

Tim sat down on the grass alongside me. I probably should have offered him my chair, but I was here first, and there were other chairs scattered about the grounds. True to form, Tim had his copy of *The Message* with him.

"Do you take that with you everywhere you go?" I asked.

He laughed. "Almost. I've never taken a shower with it, though."

I groped for something to say and was relieved when Tim moved the conversation along.

"What are you working on? Have you been charting your spiritual journey?"

"Yes," I replied. "I'm putting all my thoughts down on paper, but I'm afraid they don't fit together into any sort of plan."

"What do you mean?"

"Well, it's like this, Tim. You seem to be filled with answers, and they seem to all fit together into a single, carefully organized package. All I've got are questions. But the thing is, I believe my questions are really good, and your answers, as organized as they are, are really lousy. They stink." I couldn't believe I was saying this, but Tim didn't seem at all upset by my little outburst.

"Again, Jeff, I have to ask, what do you mean?"

I didn't know where to begin, so I just let the thoughts rush out like a flood. The kind that happens when a dam breaks.

"For starters, your answers aren't even your own. You borrow them all from that worn-out book of yours. Why do you place so much emphasis on *The Message* anyway?

"The answer is really simple, Jeff, and it should be of interest to someone such as yourself — someone who is really open to truth and to a variety of spiritual experiences. *The Message* is basically an insight from centuries ago that has been trusted by peoples from a variety of cultures throughout the world as their guidebook for finding intimacy with the God-Presence. Within its text, it tells what it can do for its readers — those who follow its clear path. It promises to show us truth, expose our rebellion, correct our mistakes, put us back together, and shape us for greater assignments on our planet. But most people don't place any priority on those kinds of things. We want to determine our own truth, and prevent our rebellion — which is really alienation — from being exposed. We don't want to be shaped for greater assignments, because our own assignments are too important to us. These greater assignments, *The Message* tells us repeatedly, involve sacrifice. Do you really care about racism and hatred, for example, or do you simply condemn them without taking any real, meaningful action? And, suppose you do take action? Is it self-serving, or is it truly a matter of caring?

"You seem to be open to its words, Jeff. In your journal, you wrote about the anti-abortion people who murder doctors on the steps of abortion clinics. *The Message* does not accept those "human" responses any more than you do, because they are not expressions of the love, peace, joy, and forgiveness we will have for each other when we are reconciled to the God-Presence."

"But, Tim," I interrupted, "why depend on this one book? What about the great spiritual writings of other times and people? All of the great cultures throughout history have given us words to live by. The Torah. The Koran. The Vedas. The Theravada canon. The Tao-te Ching. The Words of Confucius. Even modern books such as *A Course in Miracles* and..."

"And *The Celestine Prophecy*?" Tim finished.

"Yes, even *The Celestine Prophecy*."

"You seem to know a great deal about ancient teachings and religious texts, Jeff."

"I've studied them a little as part of my spiritual search. I admit I don't really understand them, but I'm not sure anyone does."

"Good point," Tim interjected. "I've studied all these and more for over twenty-three years, and I probably don't understand them any better than you do. Yet they all contain great insights.

There are remarkable teachings in each of them."

"Then why don't you teach from them at Tocayo?" I asked.

"Let's say, Jeff, that you believe — and, in truth, know for a fact — that the entire English language is based on 26 letters — A to Z. And let's say that someone comes along and tries to convince you that there are more than 26 letters. There are also letters 27, and 28, and 29, and 30 — whatever they are. Is that going to change the fact that you can read and write the English language using only the 26 original letters?"

"No," I said. But I didn't see his point.

"Let's say, then, that I know that all of life — anything that is really important or has value to me as a human being — can be described and defined and understood and evaluated on the basis of a written set of insights called *The Message*. Why do I need to add to it? Why do I need to look for additional insights from books, or novels, or rocks, or tea leaves, or whatever else you can name? Why don't I just stick with what works?"

I didn't know how to respond, and Tim obviously knew that.

"The only reason I rely on *The Message*, and the only reason I keep turning to it, and returning to it, is because it satisfies me totally and completely. I don't need new letters beyond A to Z to express my thoughts to you, and I don't need anything beyond *The Message* in order for the God-Presence to express to me a Love and Light so great that I am at last able to break the bonds of alienation and self-centeredness that had destroyed every relationship I had tried to build."

With that, Tim stood up. "I'm due back at my office for the next conference," he said. "Don't forget that our afternoon seminar is in less than forty-five minutes."

"I won't," I promised.

I watched Tim walk back to the main building, then opened my journal to write. But when I picked up my pen, I felt a cramp in my hand. In fact, it downright hurt. I closed the book and just sat there, until a brilliant idea hit me! It was a beautiful day — perfect for a walk in the wooded area south of the lake.

I took a left just past my cabin, on a narrow trail that appeared to lead into the most dense part of the woods. It was unbelievably quiet in the midst of this aromatic blend of oak, birch, and northern pine. There was so little breeze that the leaves weren't even rustling. I'd hear birds and, occasionally, the sound of a squirrel scratching its way up a tree.

Within five or six minutes I reached the edge of the woods and stepped out into a field covered with tall grasses and vividly colored wild flowers. To my right, near the south edge of the woods, I spotted two white-tailed deer — a doe and her fawn. Dad was nowhere to be seen. I stood there, frozen in place, and watched them. Suddenly, they made a dash for the protective cover of the woods. I don't know what alarmed them. I felt it wasn't anything I had done, though they may have finally picked up my scent.

I ventured out into the field, despite the lack of a clearly defined trail. Until this experience, I had never appreciated the simple beauty of a field of grasses and flowers. I preferred the stateliness of forests, the power of ocean waves crashing into the shore, and the implied strength of jutting rock formations and bold mountains. But a grass field? A small spark could turn it into bare, charred land in nearly an instant. In the terms of ancient Eastern thought and religion, fields like this simply contribute to the continual regeneration of the universe. Participating in the ritual by striking a match would result in my twentieth-century arrest, I was sure.

I had completely lost track of the time, so I shouldn't have been surprised by the fact that I was about as far from the main building as I could be when I heard the faint sound of the chime announcing the afternoon seminar. When I slipped into the back of the meeting room — out of breath from the rapid pace of my return hike — Tim was already speaking, reading again from *The Message*.

"All this time, the older son was out in the field. When the day's work was done he came in. As he approached the house, he heard the music and dancing. Calling over one of the houseboys, he asked what was going on. He told him, 'Your brother came home. Your father has ordered a feast — barbecued beef! — because he has him home safe and sound.'"

It didn't take me long to figure out that was the next chapter in the father-son story that Tim had spelled out in considerable detail over the past few days.

Tim continued, ignoring my late arrival. *"The older brother stalked off in an angry sulk and refused to join in. His father came out and tried to talk to him, but he wouldn't listen. The son said, 'Look how many years I've stayed here serving you, never giving you one moment of grief, but have you ever thrown a party for me and my friends? Then this son of yours who has thrown away your money on whores shows up and you go all out with a feast!'*

"His father said, 'Son, you don't understand. You're with me all the time, and everything that's mine is yours — but this is a wonderful time, and we had to celebrate. This brother of yours was dead, and he's alive! He was lost, and he's found!'"

Tim closed his book and looked up. "That's the end of the story. There is no more to it. But, now, as best I can, I want to put it all together for you, in my own words, so that you can fully understand what it teaches about the God-Presence.

"Here's a young man who wasn't happy with life at home. He wanted to see and taste and experience the world. He knows he has some big money coming from his wealthy dad, so he asks for it early.

"Off he goes to Paris or perhaps Monte Carlo. He gambles. He drinks fine wines. He's into drugs. He lives in a lavish penthouse and has servants waiting on him hand and foot. If he's feeling lonely, he heads down to the bar and picks up a woman. It doesn't matter if he has to pay for her services — he can afford it. Of course, he makes a lot of new friends in his new life. They hang around him because he throws a great party.

"But this guy doesn't know the first thing about budgeting or investments, and it doesn't take long for him to blow all his money. It's the same story as Haiti's former dictator, Baby Doc, don't you think?

"Before long, he's kicked out of his penthouse for failing to pay his rent. He can't afford even the cheapest hotel, so he's forced to live on the streets. His so-called friends turn their backs on him. He's going through withdrawal. He is near starvation, and he's bleeding from the open sores of street diseases, when something occurs to him. Though he has no formal education, he does have a marketable skill. His dad is a farmer, he was a farmer, so he figures he can get a job on a big farm. Why, he may even get hired as the manager!

"He trudges from farm to farm, to no avail. Along the roadside, he finds enough wild berries to stay alive. His shoes are falling apart and his feet are scorched from the hot pavement. He looks so wretched that he can't even hitch a ride on passing farm trucks.

"Finally, the owner of a very small farm tells him that he could use some help taking care of the hogs — but he'll have to sleep in the hog barn because the farmhouse is so cramped. Now, I don't know if you've ever spent any time with hogs, but they stink something awful. They are incredibly dirty, and working around them would make you dirty.

"One night, as he makes a pillow out of straw and lays down to sleep — just a few feet from the biggest, smelliest swine you could imagine — he starts to think. 'My father treats his hired hands a whole lot better than this. In fact, he's a model employer — kind, considerate, fair. I know what I'll do. I'll go back to him and beg for mercy, and I'll tell him that I'd like to be one of his farmhands so that I can pay him back.'

"The next morning, off he goes. Still no shoes. Still hungry. Still bleeding. He stands on a street corner in front of the most fashionable stores in the city and begs for money. After days without sleep, he finally scrapes together the cash to buy an airline ticket back home. He doesn't even have enough money to take a bus out to his dad's farm, so he walks the eighteen mile trek from the airport.

"His father must have lived every day hoping and praying his son would come back. He must really have loved him; he must have walked out in front of his great house every day, hoping to spot his son making his way up the road. Because *The Message* says that while he was still a long way off, Dad saw his son and ran out to greet him and gave him a big bear hug. He wrapped his arms around this big, stinking, bleeding, sweating run-away as if nothing had ever happened.

"The son didn't exactly know what to make of this, so he simply delivered his carefully rehearsed lines: 'Dad, I know I've done terrible things and I don't even deserve to be your son anymore. But I beg you to let me be one of your hired hands and live in the bunkhouse and try to repay what I owe you.

" 'No way,' said Dad. 'I'm throwing a party in your honor. I forgive you for being self-centered. I'm not going to punish you for your mistakes. I love you — you don't have any reason to be alienated from me. I'm just grateful that you're alive and that you've come home.'

"Can you imagine such a thing? Can you picture such forgiveness? Maybe at some time in the past, you've had a falling out with your parents or your children or your spouse. Can you forgive them — can they forgive you? Can you erase the bitter words? Can the memories of abuse be wiped away? Is something like this really possible?

"Well, Dad threw the party for his son. And when the other son came home from a tough day in the fields, he heard all the noise and partying and wondered what was going on. When he discovered that the celebration was in honor of his deadbeat drunk of a brother, he got mad and started yelling at his father.

"About all his father could say was, 'My son was given up for dead, but now he's alive.' I imagine he may have even added these words: 'Son, I'm celebrating, just as I would celebrate if I feared *you* were dead, and *you* showed up alive.'

"If it's possible, try to place yourself in this story. Imagine that you had spent your entire inheritance on drugs and gambling and on 'buying' friends and sex partners. Imagine that the father in the story is really the God-Presence. Would you be welcomed with open arms? Would the God-Presence be watching each day for you, hoping to catch sight of you making your way home?

"Imagine that you're Michael Bowman, and that you've killed

someone in cold blood. Would you be welcomed home with open, eager arms? Would a party be held in your honor?

"My dear men and women, Michael can answer all of those questions with a confident 'YES!' When you are able to do the same, you will be on the path to your personal discovery of the greatest spiritual insight ever revealed."

Tim stepped down from the podium and slowly made his way toward the door.

"So that's IT, huh, Tim?" I thought to myself. "All of this searching of mine all comes down to 'Take-the-Shortest-Road-Home-to-the-God-Presence'? I don't think so, Tim. That's too easy. If it were really that easy, everyone would be doing it."

I knew there was more to it. I knew that what I was looking for was a synthesis of the entire range of human thought and experience — art, science, medicine, religion, philosophy, nature, poetry, literature, emotion, feelings, pain, love — only by discovering all of these blended together in harmony at the end of my spiritual journey will I have satisfied my longing. Why did these elements need to compete among themselves? Why couldn't they fuse together for me, the way they seem to for so many of those who adhere to various Eastern teachings? I caught a glimpse of this philosophy in my travels. If these are the underlying thoughts of so many people from so many cultures, there must be something to them.

Where Next?

I was the last to leave the meeting room. The thing to do now, I decided, was to get back to work on my journal. I had worked hard on it all day and had only gotten as far as my trip to Teotihuacán.

Once in my cabin, I kicked off my shoes and settled comfortably on my bed, propping my pillow against the side wall instead of the headboard. I reviewed my earlier entries to see where I had left off.

JOURNAL ENTRY — THURSDAY BEFORE DINNER

I suppose it's not my place to judge, but I really think that Tim's spiritual journey has been rather superficial and shortsighted. If this guy has studied anything about the cultures, philosophies, and religions of the past and present, he certainly hasn't let us in on any of their truths. My guess is that he's never been to Egypt, China, Mexico, or even any Native American ruins in his pursuit of truth. He's just buried his nose in his book.

True, I didn't experience all the things I had hoped to on my trip to Mexico. Some of it was what you might even call unpleasant.

When we had seen all there was to see at Teotihuacán, we returned to the Hotel "Majestic". Our group decided to meet for dinner at the restaurant on the top floor. We sat together and for the longest time talked about almost everything except our trip to the pyramids.

I was dying to know what had happened to the others during the day — did they find meditation easy? Did they feel the spiritual energy of the sacred places we had visited? What were their experiences and backgrounds? How did all of this type of spiritual talk fit into their understanding of life? Was a door of contact with spiritual realities opening in my own life?

The food was great, and the salsa was really picante — none of that New York City stuff here. No taco fast food restaurant in the States could hold a garlic-flavored pepper-filled candle to this restaurant!

Finally, toward the end of dinner, the conversation turned to our day. I sensed that everyone had found the experience so personal that they were hesitant to share their feelings. Those who did still kept many specific details to themselves. They talked about how energized they were from their time of meditation. Some of them spoke of the awe they felt from standing on sacred ground. Others complained about the hot, stuffy van. I felt that I had gotten as much out of the day as anyone.

But I was fading fast. My early wake-up call,

combined with all the hours in the sun, had made me eager for a good night's sleep. I excused myself from the table, and by 9:00 P.M., I was history. The traffic sounds outside my window slowly faded away as I drifted off to sleep.

Around midnight I woke up suddenly in a cold sweat. Strange sensations went up and down my body. At first I thought I may be experiencing death. You know, drifting off toward a bright light while I tingled all over. Then I thought it may be the visitation of an ancient god, angered that I had invaded his sacred space at Teotihuacán.

As it turned out, this *was* a visitation! Montezuma had taken his revenge, and I ran for the bathroom door, almost missing the light switch on the way into this urgently needed little room.

For the rest of the night I had plenty of time for meditation. Seated on the porcelain throne, I had time to count every square in the ceiling tiles and rethink everything I had eaten and drunk during the day. These thoughts didn't do much good — I had experimented with enough different foods to invoke the presence of any local bacteria.

Yuk! How horrible can a person feel? I hate that pink stuff, yet I slugged it down. (A whole bottle before it was over.) I returned to my bed — briefly — and quite a few times. The bells outside chimed at all sorts of weird hours, and a drunk serenaded the hotel at about 2:45 A.M. Two police cars passed by with sirens screaming about 3:15, and finally — it must've been around 4:00 —

I fell asleep. The trumpets sounded at 6:00 and I again leaped out of bed — this time heading directly for the magic door.

By late morning, I was almost back to normal. I had missed the morning tour of the anthropological museum, and frankly, I didn't give a rip. But I was able to catch up with the group for our tour of the Templo Mayor in the afternoon — "conveniently located close to your hotel" — according to the brochure.

I made another exciting discovery that afternoon. Don't use public bathrooms in Mexico unless absolutely necessary. The "absolutely" only happened once before I was able to slip away from the group and head back to the Majestic.

That evening, I was brave enough to go back to the restaurant. No picante sauce, though, and none of the local delicacies. The waiter had this big grin on his face as I ordered toast and 7-UP. I believed I was ready for tomorrow's adventures, although I thought it might be a good idea to steal a roll of toilet paper from my room before I checked out of the hotel in the morning.

At 6:00 A.M. sharp, I was again blasted out of bed by the trumpet call of the Mexican army. These guys need a music teacher! They blared out the same terrible march every day — out of tune, out of sync. The Mexican flag was hoisted, and by the time they had finished blaring and marching, I was up for the day. I was careful to brush my teeth using bottled water. I didn't need another unwelcome visit from Señor Montezuma.

After a quick breakfast of chilequiles and strong coffee, we checked out of the hotel. Our bags were again stuffed in our laps in the mini-van. As we drove, Manuel explained that we could not live at peace in a land where we understood none of its spiritual roots. These roots are bound together, in the Americas, with suffering. The indigenous peoples of the Americas have suffered a lot. They've struggled with the fight to stay alive, they've struggled with the continuous wars that they've had among themselves and with others, and they've battled against the religions forced upon them by spiritual and political leaders.

The invasion of the Europeans brought great hardship, as well as new gods — gods and spirits that did not know the land nor the importance of the heritage upon the land. This new religion sought to destroy the former ways of life. The invaders enslaved, they broke the spirit, and they destroyed the health of those they captured.

On this day, we were to visit the region of one of those peoples, the Otomi of Queretaro. We were told that the drive would take about one and a half hours, but that was far from the truth. We sat for hours in suffocating traffic, trying to pick our way through a traffic jam far worse than any I had ever seen in L.A.

Directly outside my window, I had a great view of a garbage truck. There was one guy sitting on top, and he ducked every time they went underneath bridges and signs. It was almost comical. I sure hope he lived through the day.

Finally, on the northern edge of Mexico City, we broke away from the crush of traffic and I saw mile after mile of small apartment houses — what a mass of people!

As we approached Queretaro, the first major structure we saw was a modern soccer stadium. Minutes later, we were staring down at the city center with its impressive aqueduct and churches.

Our guide had a lot to say, because this was where he was born, and the Otomi were his people. Within an hour we were checked into the posh Real de Minas Hotel. The pool looked inviting, but our schedule allowed no time for even a quick dip. We were soon back on the mini-van for our tour.

Holy Cross Monastery, in the center of the city, was an important link in the "evangelization" of the indigenous peoples of Meso-America.

Manuel felt it was important that we understood the roots of the spread of Catholicism throughout New Spain, and this Franciscan training center had been instrumental in that process. Missionaries left this place to work with the people of Mexico and the surrounding territories controlled by Spain — walking on foot from this city in central Mexico to the south and far to the north. In fact, the city of San Francisco, California, had been one of the mission churches started by these friars.

We walked through the monastery in awe — though perhaps not because of the gilt altars and beautiful pieces of art. The wonderment I was experiencing was that a place I had never heard of had been so significant

in changing a continent and the lives of millions of
people — for untold generations. And I had never
known! I had been walking in a spiritual vacuum,
thinking that nothing of the history of the land actually
touched my daily existence.

I was struck by the beautiful walls, cisterns, and
aqueduct. Not only were they all beautifully
engineered, but I was impressed with the amount of
slavery that would have been necessary to see such
structures completed "for the glory of God."

I wondered what kinds of curses were said against
the gods of the Europeans from the dying breath of
slaves? What were their last thoughts as they lay
ravaged by the diseases of Europe? Where were their
gods in the midst of all of this pain?

Leaving the monastery, we drove to the small village
of La Canada, where Manuel took us to an
unpretentious little church, nestled in the valley. To
him, the most venerated spot was a small cross in a
fenced area to the left of the front door. This cross
marked the place where Konin, leader of the Otomi, met
the Spanish and submitted to their dominance — not
only to the Spanish rule, but to the spirits of the Spanish
religion. The people were forced to build churches for
their conquerors, but vestiges of their old religions were
often plastered into the walls behind the altars. So,
when they knelt before the altars and European-crafted
statues, they would be facing the very religious pieces
that were the foundation of their own faiths. They had
started on a path of resistance that allowed them to live

and survive in this land.

From there we walked about a block to a colonial building that belonged to the village of La Canada. The historian of the city was there to meet us. An interesting and crusty old man, he took us on a tour of his office. Almost one third of the room was a representation of an Otomi altar — a strange mixture of local foods, bowls for sacrifice, and various idols.

Two large wooden carvings represented the principal gods of the Otomi — one male and one female. The female god, he told us, had many apparitions during her reign over New Spain. Otomi belief said that one of her apparitions was that of Our Lady of Guadeloupe, one of the focal points of Mexican Catholicism.

So the old religions were mixed together. The theme seemed to be, "A little of this, a little of that — whatever works at the time and place." In a way, that kind of describes my spiritual journey. There are parts of many religions and histories that I appreciate. I just don't know *if* — or *how* — they fit together.

I could tell that Manuel found this to be an energizing place. As we quietly left, he stood there with closed eyes, swaying and silently praying. It kind of made me uncomfortable, but I too wanted to be in touch with the powerful spiritual forces that I felt in this place. I wanted to stretch out and touch something real, because I had sensed very little spiritual reality in my life. I was so far from spiritual perception, and yet here I was, dealing with people who were still in touch with an ancient heritage.

A week later I was back in the office. I was sure things would be different. Monday was a bit different — but by Wednesday I couldn't remember much about the longings and the peace that I had felt in the desert outside of Mexico City. I was more miserable than before trying to get in touch with these spiritual roots. I read *The Celestine Prophecy* two more times and talked again to my accountant.

He told me about his experiences in Sedona. He said that Sedona was the place. If I couldn't find what I was looking for there, it probably couldn't be found. After all, Sedona was one of the great energy fields that had been rediscovered with the renaissance of spiritual realities. So...off I went.

I was relieved to hear the dinner chime ringing away — my writer's cramp was starting to come back in a bad way. But I had to get it all on paper. And it was like it had all happened yesterday.

On my way down to the lodge, I caught up with Bonnie. She was walking slowly, stopping occasionally to look at her surroundings. I wish we could talk at this place. She had the look of someone with a lot on her mind, and I found her quite interesting. It would be fun to sit down somewhere and become engaged in a long, wandering conversation.

Her pace picked up as I passed her, smiling. She smiled back at me and when we got to the main building, I held the door for her. Terribly old-fashioned, I suppose, but I felt she wouldn't mind. It was my "random act of kindness" for the day. Maybe an important part of one's spiritual journey is learning how to give to others.

Dinner was really great! After several days of mostly bland food, we had a linguini with a fantastic basil pesto sauce and a salad that actually had some flavor. The breadsticks even sported a hint of garlic!

There was no reason to hurry through dinner tonight. Except for logging my thoughts on Sedona, I was nearly finished with my assignment. We had a seminar after dinner, but that wasn't scheduled until 8:00. I even had some hope of getting a really good, long night of sleep.

The faces at my table displayed rested looks. Everyone seemed at peace — with themselves and with the things they had experienced at Tocayo. I began to get excited about dinner on Saturday night. In just two days, we'd all be able to talk to each other again. It would be my first chance to find out what was going on inside all these people with whom I had shared so many silent glances.

Take Mary Beth, for example. Had she, through the seminars and private conferences, or as the result of meditation or her journal entries, worked through the problems facing her marriage? Were there spiritual answers to her hurts and frustrations?

Or how about Doctor John? This guy was hard to read. He certainly didn't "let it all hang out," as they used to say when I was a kid. I hope, if nothing else, he leaves here with that greatest of all spiritual insights: "Lighten up."

Bonnie-of-Hollywood would undoubtedly be leaving this place a better person than when she came. It showed on her face.

She had a carefully planned agenda when she came here, and I'm sure it was completed. So it's back to the world of show business for her. I hope the cynical network news types don't destroy her fledgling innocence. She's had a rough life; she deserves some breaks.

I'm sure the biggest question facing the congresswoman was whether or not to run for re-election. Giving the facts surrounding some of her "activities" in the past, she could have a tough fight ahead of her. I hope Tocayo provided her with a break from her everyday stresses, and that she has reached a good decision. I guess I'll find out Saturday night.

As if we had planned it in advance, we all finished eating at about the same time and got up in a "group" to leave the dining room.

I stepped out into the fading sunlight and made the firm decision that I was NOT going to write in my journal. I hadn't been down to the lake in a couple of days. It was my assignment, I was quite certain, to make sure it was still there!

Unique cloud formations appeared to be suspended over the far end of the lake. They were a mix of low, puffy cumulus, broken stratus, and high icy cirrus. I had never seen anything like it. I assumed it meant that some kind of front was approaching. Whatever. The point is that the sun was shining intermittently through this blend of distant weather systems, and the results were stunning. I'd never seen anything like it in a photograph, or even a painting. If there was some kind of "god" behind this, he or she sure dipped the brush into a full and brilliant palette of paints.

A spot this beautiful on an evening this peaceful should have served as the focal point for every person at Tocayo. But, to my surprise, no one else was anywhere nearby. I stepped out on the dock, walked out about halfway, and sat down facing the sunset. Despite a slight chill in the air, the sun felt warm and I was comforted. I stayed in that spot until I became aware that I could easily be late for the evening seminar if I didn't make a move soon.

As it turned out, I made my move soon enough to be one of the first ones to arrive in the meeting room. I was comfortably settled as the others began to wander in, and was well into meditative thoughts when Tim walked in. He wasted no time in getting to the business at hand.

"It's been an interesting day for me today," Tim began. "I've learned a lot from you in the process of meeting with you in our conferences. More than one of you has expressed disappointment and frustration that your spiritual journeys aren't complete — that you aren't so-called 'masters' of the process of enlightenment and growth. Please don't be disappointed. You haven't failed in any way.

"*The Message* teaches us that as we make our journeys, we first feed on milk, like babies, and then we move on to more substantial diets as we grow. No matter where you are in the process of awakening to the knowledge of the God-Presence — or to your own unique awareness of the spiritual dimensions that encompass all of life — there is always more discovery ahead. The adventure is in the journey, not in the destination. The excitement is in the growing, not in the being. No matter where we come from, no matter what we learn, I believe we cannot truly 'be' until we perfectly reflect all of the wondrous qualities of the God-Presence.

"Consider the true masters the world has known. Did

Michelangelo pick up a brush for the first time and paint the ceiling of the Sistine Chapel that very day? Did Ansel Adams buy the equivalent of an Instamatic camera and instantly become a photographer of world renown? Did Carl Lewis leap out of his mother's arms and become a record-breaking athlete? Did William Shakespeare write *Macbeth* in preschool? Did Mozart sit down at a harpsichord and become one of the greatest composers the world has ever known?

"Absolutely not! You know that as well as I do, although I have to admit that Mozart perhaps came the closest to achieving the status of an 'instant master.' Even the great violinist Midori — who stunned the world with her incredible talent at a very young age — continues today to develop her skills and her sensitivity to the music.

"Don't get sucked into the lie that you can become a 'master' in a brief moment. You do not arrive at your goal the same instant you embark on your journey.

"Perhaps only the darker sides of our nature take so little effort and energy to perfect. I doubt that infants need to be taught to be self-centered — to cry and scream and demand what they want. I'm convinced that people who cheat on their spouses don't need to go to seminars to learn how to lust. And even Adolph Hitler and Joseph Stalin can't blame their hatred of innocent people and their disregard for human life on their dysfunctional pasts or poverty or poor schooling or whatever it is we like to blame our problems on these days.

"If you think back on what Michael told us, you realize that the God-Presence accepts us in the midst of the imperfections of our darker sides and creates entirely new people out of us. Now, I know some of you may actually still fear Michael. Some of you may firmly believe that he should never have been released from prison. That he should have been locked up forever. I am confident, though, that, for Michael, the old ways of living and acting died forever when Brother Duane showed him the path to knowledge of, and relationship with, the God-Presence and he accepted it.

"If you doubt the very existence of the God-Presence, you will have to seek another path to love, acceptance, and the destruction of self-centeredness. If you believe you are not alienated from others and from the spiritual force that bonds us with time and eternity, and with all we describe as the universe, then you are at a level of perception that transcends what we seek here at Tocayo. But if you are totally honest, you are among those who seek.

"Where have you sought answers? Philosophy? Science? Religion?

"You may not agree with what I'm going to say next, and if you don't, that's fine. I believe that the religions of the world have misled us terribly. Most of them have tried to convince us that we can personally do something that will assure us the desired end result, whether that end result is 'heaven' or 'nirvana' or a 'higher state of being.' They tell us that if we blow it, we're out of luck. If we believe in reincarnation, we may come back as a bug. If we don't live up to 'God's' standards, we go to hell. If we don't do this or that, we end up in suspended animation, sort of like anesthesia.

"If you've looked at the world around you, and if you're honest with yourself, you'll have to admit that we've all blown it. I've found that most of my giving to others is really for the purpose of building up myself. Most of my self-sacrifice is really sacrifice for myself.

"*The Message* teaches that we are the objects of incredible love and unfathomable affection. We are urgently desired. We are desperately sought. The God-Presence is much like the father in the story I've been reading. We can be stinky, sweaty, grime-covered, thankless, unkempt, impoverished, selfish men and women, and the God-Presence will still welcome us home. We can cheat on our income taxes, stomp on our marriage vows, destroy our relationships, and disgust our society, and still find spiritual peace. The love energy of the God-Presence is stronger than our self-betrayal."

Tim paused for a moment. "This has been a pretty heavy day for all of us, I think. Tomorrow, we're going to be thinking about what we can expect when we are flooded by the unseen spirit of the God-Presence.

"In the meantime, get some rest. No new assignments. Just meditate on the concepts we've explored."

Tim was perceptive — I had to concede that fact. He had barely stepped down from the podium when many of us stood up and began to leave. It was obvious we were tired and ready for bed. Truth is, I couldn't wait! That lumpy bed was going to feel great tonight.

In reality, though, that night of much-deserved rest never came to be. I tossed, I turned. I got up, switched on the lights, and wrote in my journal. I read. I paced. I did everything but sleep. It occurred to me that if Connie were here, she'd have kicked me out of the cabin to pursue my scattered thoughts out in the woods. Connie, bless her well-ordered soul, loves her sleep and doesn't let much of anything get in its way.

Even when the kids were little, she made me get up with them in the middle of the night. I know that's expected of your basic nineties guy, but it was still pretty weird seven and ten years ago, when Amy and Josh were born. Connie solved the problem (or so she thought) with that marvelous invention that has liberated millions of moms from their middle-of-the-night duties — the breast pump. I don't care what they say, the little devils can still distinguish subtle differences in the product depending on whether it's presented to them in a bottle or in the original packaging.

It had been a day filled with deep thoughts about my searchings. I was still filled with complex and conflicting thoughts, and I didn't want even one to escape before I had the opportunity to commit them to my memory, or, better yet, to my journal.

JOURNAL ENTRY — THURSDAY NIGHT ...OR IS IT FRIDAY MORNING?

Even if I leave this retreat no more spiritually aware than when I arrived here, I know this will have been good for me. The peace and quiet have been healing qualities in the midst of my troubled life.

I'm still not buying into this "Message" thing, but the whole discussion has helped me more accurately reflect on my journey to this point in my life.

For one thing, I'm not so sure I've learned anything from pyramids, rocks, vortexes, and plants. So what if rocks have energy and plants have auras? I really doubt that any father awaited the return of a rock or a plant with open arms and an eager, wildly beating heart. Let alone a "God-Presence."

I've journeyed to the best rocks on this planet. Great

rocks. I mean, Sedona is nothing to sneeze at. Supposedly all the energy of that part of the country is focused on the great vortexes near Sedona. But did I really sense anything different there, or was I simply expected to sense something because the Dunker supposedly did and because whoever told him about it supposedly did? I guess I'd rather be loved than achieve intimate contact with mysterious energy forces in rocks or trees. I guess I'd really prefer to put an end to the various forms of alienation that exist in my life as I'm living it today.

My conclusion is that I'm worth more than plants, trees, and rocks. I'm superior to inanimate, unthinking things, no matter how much energy they possess.

My other conclusion is that I'd really like to get a good night's sleep.

I set aside my journal and stared out my window into the darkness. In the distance, I could see the faint glow of another light. Someone in one of the cabins by the lake must be thinking, writing, and perhaps pacing, too. For only the second time since I had arrived at Tocayo, I wished I could interrupt the silence with a radio. I wished I could tune in some all-night talk show and enjoy a little mindless company. I wished there were someone I could talk to...someone who could give me more time than the few minutes I had with Tim each day.

Though I valued all the alone time that Tocayo afforded me, I'm basically not a loner. I thrive on the activity of the people at work, out on business trips, and even at home.

A glass of milk and some Oreo cookies sure would have hit the spot. But I was trapped with my thoughts in a foodless, noiseless, peopleless cabin. Bathroomless, too. About 2:30 in the morning, I took the short hike down to the shower building to take care of business.

There was no real reason to hurry back to my cabin, so I paused along the trail to listen for "night sounds" and to gaze up at the stars. The wonderful thing about remote places like the Habitat — so removed from the city — is that the stars and planets have such a wonderful opportunity to display their awesome glory. With no bright city lights to compete with the heavenly lights, they multiplied in number, and intensified in brilliance.

Did I feel small and insignificant? Yes. But if Tim is right and there is a God-Presence who has an all-consuming love for me, perhaps I'm not as small and insignificant as I think I am.

Until I stepped back into the warmth of the cabin, I hadn't even been aware of the chill that was spreading through the night air. "I sure will sleep great now," I thought.

The Quiet
Revelation

The darkness of night was slowly dissolving into another crisp, clear dawn as a major insight "dawned" on me. I really had not slept at all the previous night. Not one minute. This was not just my imagination.

Yet, I didn't feel tired. In fact, I felt invigorated. Ready to get up and go.

I threw on my favorite sweats, which by now had acquired that special flavor I associate with Josh's gym bag when he brings it home at the end of the school week. I headed down to the shower. Plenty of hot water today. I bet I beat everyone by at least a half an hour.

Back at my cabin, I changed into what appeared to be my last set of clean clothes. Because I still had another full day to go after today, I'd have to wear something a second time. I was quite sure it wouldn't be my sweats. "At least deodorant and after shave can mask some of the smell," I thought. That reminded me of when I was a kid. We had a limited supply of soft water — rainwater, actually — which we collected in an old-fashioned cistern, so we couldn't bathe or shower more than once a week. My father solved the problem by daily splashing on some Old Spice — a fragrance that still makes me choke to this day.

I considered taking a walk down to the lake, or perhaps out past the wooded part of the property to the fields I had explored yesterday. But I decided instead to head for the library, journal in hand.

"I hope Tim isn't there," I thought as I opened the outside door to the main building. I almost turned back, but continued down the hall. I glanced at the sign-up sheet for the meditation room, and it occurred to me again that I hadn't spent time in that room since I'd been here. If I didn't do it today, I'd never have the chance, so I decided to sign up for the first open time.

I had no idea this little room had become the life of the party. The first open slot the whole day was at 10:30 at night. My first thought was, "With no sleep last night, I'll never make it." But I wanted to at least be able to SAY I'd done the meditation thing, so I signed up.

The library was completely dark. It seemed curious that the library was the one room I had been in that had no outside windows — it was more or less in the center of the building, surrounded by the other rooms. I flipped on the lights and scanned the shelves for a book I thought might hold my interest. I chose a biography of President Harry Truman written by his daughter, Margaret. Why, I'm not sure, since this guy was president long before I was born, and was, in my opinion, just average in his performance of the duties of the office, from what I had learned of him in school. I settled in what I had decided was the most comfortable chair in the room and opened the book to the first page. "Copyright 1963, 1972 , Morrow, New York. All

Rights Reserved," I read. Well, that sure got me hooked!

The table of contents, I knew, was just ahead. What excitement! I couldn't wait! Before I could read and reflect on the chapter titles, Tim walked into the room. "Great," I thought, "I should have come here at 2:00 A.M. when I couldn't sleep. I bet Tim wouldn't have shown up that early!"

"Hey, Jeff," Tim said. I thought for a brief instant that the proper response to "Hey, Jeff," was probably something like, "Yo, Bro', what's happnin' this A.M.?" But I ruled that out and said, "Good morning, Tim."

"Sleep all right?" he asked. I still say he's a mind reader. Or maybe it was the bags under my eyes.

"As a matter of fact, no," I replied.

"I'm sorry to hear that."

"Well," I continued hesitantly, "you might say it's your fault."

"Why's that?" he asked.

"For starters," I said, "you don't let me begin my day with coffee, so I don't get off to an alert start. Then, by the middle of the day, I'm dragging. By midafternoon, your probing questions and difficult assignments inspire my second wind, and by nightfall, I can't sleep."

"Oh, is that all?" Tim chuckled.

I didn't respond.

"Have you wondered why we stay away from caffeine, chemicals and preservatives, and serve healthy, natural, fat-free foods instead?" Tim asked.

"Well, I assume it's because we gain more energy from natural foods."

"Not exactly. It's because our bodies are the temples of the God-Presence. We choose not to defile something of such

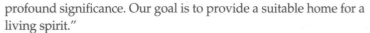

profound significance. Our goal is to provide a suitable home for a living spirit."

I was puzzled — and, in some respects, a little spooked by this talk. "Does that mean that *we* are the God-Presence? That we are all, in a manner of speaking, God?"

"No," Tim responded as he flipped through the pages of *The Message*, searching for something or other. "It means that when we come into the intended relationship with the God-Presence, we become a dwelling place of the most dynamic energy in the universe. But this energy does not force its way into our being. We have to invite it in. Let me read this short insight. '*Look at me,*' says God-Presence. '*I stand at the door and knock. If you hear me call and open the door, I'll come right in and sit down to supper with you.*' "

"That doesn't sound like an energy standing at the door of my being. It sounds like a Saturday night dinner party," I interjected.

"For someone who has tuned himself into the mystical energy of plants and rocks and special spiritual places — mere objects which can't speak to you at all — you don't sound too willing to listen to the words of the God-Presence who has spoken to us through *The Message*. This is mystical, not literal. It's figurative speech. But at least the words exist in print. We're not dealing with an imaginary manuscript from Peru here."

"You know, Tim," I offered, "I'm not alone in my doubts about what you've been teaching us these past few days, and I'm also not alone in gaining valuable insights from *The Celestine Prophecy*. It doesn't matter to me whether the manuscript exists or not. I've learned things about myself and others that will have meaning to me the rest of the days of my life. So don't be so quick to put it down."

"Please remember, Jeff, that I'm not here to judge you or your personal journey, or the books you read, or the realities you've discovered. That's not what we're about here. *The Message* says that the God-Presence won't walk over anyone's feelings or push them into a corner. Instead, they are given the opportunity to discover the intimacy and hope they long for.

"So our objective, Jeff, is simply to offer the path to true, satisfying intimacy with the God-Presence. If you can find the deep relationships that I honestly believe we all desire through spiritual pilgrimages, or inspiring rock formations, or best-selling books, that's fine. If your inner needs aren't met in those ways, perhaps we can help by sharing what we've discovered about entering a relationship with the God-Presence."

I pressed him. "What have you discovered, Tim? What do you really know for sure? What can any of us know for sure? Don't you have doubts?"

"Jeff, there was a time in my life when I was nothing but a huge collection of doubts. The only God I had ever heard about was a distant, remote, unfeeling, gray-bearded old fellow who sat on a cloud somewhere up in the sky, ready to zap me with lightning bolts if I stepped out of line. I wasn't into that kind of thing at all. I knew I didn't need him or anything he stood for. Frankly, I saw him as a big zero.

"But one thing I did know. From a very early age, I craved intimate, caring relationships with people. Like most of us, my parents offered my first hope of achieving that. But my father was an alcoholic and was frequently unemployed. My mom had to work to hold things together financially for the family, so she seldom had time to relate to us kids.

"As the years went on, Dad's drinking got completely out of control, and so did his emotions. When I was thirteen or fourteen,

I would go to school with so many bruises that I faked notes from my mother so I wouldn't have to take physical education classes. I didn't want anyone to see my injuries in the locker room. One time, my father threw me against a kitchen chair so violently that I got a huge, fat, bleeding lip. I pleaded not to go to school, but went anyway and told my classmates that I had gotten hit by a baseball."

The breakfast chime rang, but we both ignored it. This was the most time I had spent with Tim, and I hoped he didn't care about breakfast.

"You hungry?" he asked. "Do you want to head down to breakfast?"

"It doesn't matter to me," I answered. "I appreciate having this time to talk to you. You've never really told any of us anything about your life."

"Well, I didn't intend to go on and on, Jeff."

"Really, it's okay. So...what ultimately happened with your parents?"

"My dad eventually left. I was about fifteen at the time. We never heard from him again. When I was in college, I got a phone call from a hospital in Pittsburgh. They said he was dead. I was so angry with him...so hurt by him...I didn't even go to his funeral."

"What about your mom?"

"She continued working hard all her life. She held the family of four kids together. She even helped us all with college, as much as she could. Fortunately, all four of us received scholarships. She died about eight years ago. We were all there for her. All except my brother, Rob, who was killed in Vietnam. We all loved her. I thought the world of her, but I never really got to know her. I really regret that."

Tim's eyes were misting, so I thought that would be the end of his story. But he went on.

"Beginning in my senior year of high school, and then throughout college, I honestly believed I could experience intimacy through relationships with women. My idea of intimacy was to seduce as many of them as possible. Intimacy, to me, had nothing to do with knowing someone's thoughts and heart and soul. It was just sex. That was the deepest form of intimacy there could be, I thought. But every time I left a woman's arms, I felt as alone and empty as when I had first laid down with her.

"My last year of college, I met a very special lady, and I was convinced she was the one for me. We had good times together, the sex was great, and I was beginning to realize that there could be a form of intimacy to be enjoyed beyond sex.

"One spring weekend, an old lover of hers who had been going to school at Stanford flew into town and literally stole my dream girl right out from under me. And I *do* mean that in the most literal sense you could imagine.

"Without going into detail about other relationships, let me just say that it seemed that every time I got close to someone — anyone — they let me down. And I really never found the intimate relationships I was looking for. So I decided to look within myself...searching for a way to find peace, satisfaction, and contentment within myself. I embarked on a study of the great philosophies and religions of the world, concentrating on Eastern thought, and the concept of yin-yang, the two complementary forces that are exhibited in all aspects of life."

I interrupted. "I've studied that, too. I used to stare at that symbol — the two halves of the circle, dark and light — and ponder what it really meant in terms of my existence."

"What did you discover?" Tim asked.

"Well, not much really, yet. But I'm still learning."

"In my case, I firmly believed that my 'yang,' the male half of the symbol, had a 'yin' that I had not yet found. I perceived that to be female, but I wasn't sure I would find my complement in a single female figure. I would not be complete, I thought, until the circle that represented my life was whole.

"As I studied and searched, I traveled to many of the places you have gone — and a few you haven't. I've been to Japan, to Tibet, to India. I have seen the seven wonders of the ancient world and more.

"But it wasn't until I went to a place much like Tocayo Habitat that I stumbled upon an insight that has literally transformed my life. Completed it is a better term."

"And that insight," I asked, "is from *The Message*?"

"Yes, clearly so," Tim answered. "*The Message* tells us that the God-Presence is the only one who can make us complete — who can become the true complementary counterpart to our half of the circle."

"How do you prove this?" I asked. "How do you know that the God-Presence is more than a myth?" I wanted to know.

"You cannot know until you set aside your doubt and disbelief. *The Message* teaches that wondrous things are in store for those who believe without seeing. The truth is, you cannot know until you know." Tim got to his feet. "I'm sorry, Jeff, I have conferences beginning in just a couple of minutes. I'll be talking about some of these things in our morning seminar, though."

I watched him leave — with a puzzled expression on my face, I'm sure — then put the Truman biography back on the shelf where I found it. What did he mean, "You cannot know until you know"?

If the dawn had been any indication of what the rest of this day was going to be like, I knew I didn't want to spend my time in a stuffy library. Sure enough, I stepped outside into the nicest day I had seen all week. There was an open lawn chair just north of the lodge, next to the carefully tended gardens. I sat down and immediately noticed the presence of very active honeybees. They didn't appear to have any interest in my arrival, so I studied them for a few minutes. "Amazing," I thought. "Here's this insect that has many useful purposes — making honey and cross-pollinating flowers among them — yet its sting is instantly deadly to some people who have allergic reactions." It all made me wonder if I had some complex purpose in life that I had not yet stumbled upon, or if I was simply born to sting and be stung.

JOURNAL ENTRY — FRIDAY MORNING

As I sit here studying my surroundings, I wonder if my eyes are taking in the beauty of flowers and plants that wouldn't exist without honeybees. Nature is so remarkably complex. Each species contributes to the existence of another. Because of bees, flowers come into being. And because of flowers, bees are able to feed themselves and nourish their young.

The balance is so delicate that it amazes me that we humans continue to disturb it so blatantly. We're destroying the planet that sustains our lives, and we do it simply for greed, or to further our own selfish political or philosophical or social agenda.

If the human race is still evolving, the evidence suggests that it's evolving in the wrong direction. We're not getting better; we're just getting better at getting for ourselves.

Some politicians suggest that the underlying reason for our human problems is the economic disparity between the "haves" and the "have nots." If we could just give money and housing to the poor by taking away excess money from the rich, then everything would work out fine.

Others have offered education as the solution. Teach the "have nots." Train them. Create opportunity. Level the playing field.

A few good-hearted souls tell us that philanthropy is the answer. Give money to community drives, stage a concert for a disease, hold a country music extravaganza for a particular group experiencing hardship, have a telethon, send grain to a third-world country. Whatever.

At one time or another, I've bought into all of those ideas myself. I've plastered my car with bumper stickers that have encouraged my fellow commuters to "Save the Whales," "Save the Rain Forests," "Save the Inner Cities," and "Save the Wetlands." You name it, I've wanted to save it.

I'm not saying I'm wrong about all this. I'm just finally realizing that it's not enough. It's humankind that needs the saving. From ourselves, more than anything, I guess.

I'm starting to see Tim's point. I'm willing to accept the premise that it's our selfishness and self-centeredness that's behind all the wars and hatred and crime.

Will money or education prevent a drunken father from beating his kid senseless or sexually molesting his young daughter? Will saving a whale prevent a rape or a shooting in the school yard? Will wearing a ribbon stop the spread of AIDS? Will sending millions or billions of dollars in foreign aid guarantee basic human rights for all?

All these ongoing human problems, I think, might be the symptoms of a deeper, deadlier disease. And about all we know how to do is point out the symptoms. We know what to call them. Yet we've never given a name to the disease. Is it reasonable to think that it could be called "self-centeredness"?

I think it might be too much to expect that Tim's "God-Presence" offers the answers to all of life's questions as he seems to believe. His "yin" may have met his "yang" through the God-Presence, but I doubt that it could be that simple for me. I'm willing to learn, though, how the God-Presence impacts people in their self-centered ways, because I want to be more than a part of the human problem. I want to be part of the human solution.

Almost everyone arrived in the meeting room for our morning seminar before the last chime had faded away. As the week had progressed, we all exhibited an increased expectancy every time we went to the meeting room or to a conference with Tim. We smiled more openly when we passed each other on the trails or congregated in the showers or gathered for meals. In a sense, we were becoming a small family of sorts, even though we hadn't spoken to each other for several days.

So it was a little ironic to me — and not at all coincidental, I believe — that Tim's topic for the Friday morning seminar was "family." He had an urgency in his steps to the podium; an urgency I also heard in his voice. "This must really be important stuff," I thought. I listened attentively to every word and took careful notes.

"When we enter into right relationship with the God-Presence," Tim began, "we become part of an eternal, celestial family. But gaining the right to belong to that family is not enough. Because in this dimension — within the confines of our earthly bonds — we must actually *become* family.

"Many of you are turned off by the word 'family.' You have terrible memories that haunt you — memories of physical and mental abuse, memories of painful divorces, or of broken relationships with those who should have been the closest and the most caring people in your lives.

"I want you to know that I understand how you feel. I was raised in what we now call a 'dysfunctional family.' I was abused as a child. My father was an alcoholic who deserted my mom and me and my brother and sisters. I discovered later that the reason for all this pain was really self-centeredness. Not even one member of my family knew of the God-Presence. We were all completely selfish and we all paid the price for that. It wasn't that the knowledge of God-Presence wasn't available to us had we truly searched, it was simply that we rejected the entire notion that there could be a spiritual dimension to the universe.

"As a result, even when my being was filled with the God-Presence, and I was empowered for my life journey, it was difficult for me to believe and understand that I was now part of a new family.

"Today, I understand that I am a member of a family with many brothers and sisters who have turned away from their self-centeredness, and who desire to put an end to alienation in their relationships. They want to lead the world into a new age of harmony with the God-Presence. *The Message* says we discover our rightful place in the family when we show people how to cooperate instead of compete and fight — when we go to those who have wronged us and we forgive them — when we help others without caring if we personally gain something as a result.

"So becoming true brothers and sisters means learning how to be brothers and sisters. We were, but we also had to become.

"There are many other things we become when the God-Presence fills us and surrounds us. But we don't see them or understand them or accept them all in an instant. The whole process is one of first belonging, then becoming.

"Naturally, one of our basic frustrations is that we are all romantics. We hope to magically see the end of the story from the beginning, in about the same time that it takes us to watch a rented video movie. Somehow, we expect to be more complete in our insights than the master mystics and spiritual leaders of the past. They found a path that our generation and the one that came before rejected. But we were raised in a secularized and spiritually dead generation because we thought we could achieve all of the best results on our own.

"Today, many of us are discovering that we cannot do it on our own. We are learning that we will never justify our own existence based on our spiritual insights, nor are we capable of building satisfying physical or spiritual relationships without the action of the God-Presence. Yet even when we perceive that we cannot do this ourselves, we still try to dictate how it will happen.

"With the culture of our 'instant society' all around us, we insist that somehow the spiritual life must begin springing up within us, and then flow to maturity in a matter of days or weeks. The 'instant' of our society and culture has stymied and stunted our spiritual growth, even after we have found the path to spiritual renaissance. Somehow, we believe that our spiritual needs are going to be satisfied immediately — in the same way that we can make an instant cup of cappuccino, or instantly access information on our computers, or obtain instant credit. This is reinforced by the fact that, since the early fifties, our society has been programmed by television to think that with a few commercial breaks, all human problems and dilemmas can be solved in just half an hour.

"Don't buy into the premise that your spiritual needs will be answered immediately. Remember, most of us here have taken the time to attend seminars that promised mind control, meditation, new spiritual realities, or the ultimate in New Age enlightenment. Our expectations, fed by the hype surrounding these programs and seminars, led us to believe that we would instantly become mature in our spiritual lives and perceptions if we would only buy another tape series, read a few more of their books, or take an additional weekend course. We were hoping to discover something meaningful and lasting simply by investing a few hours and a few — or sometimes many — dollars. There are people who have gotten rich off of our vulnerability and desire for a spiritual 'quick-fix.'

"We need to understand that the God-Presence asks us nothing more than that we to learn to walk before we run — that we build a mutual relationship of complete trust and confidence. That relationship does not come without cost — you will have to invest time. You will have to be committed. Unless you become a dedicated learner at the feet of the God-Presence, you will never find the lasting peace you desire.

"To become the satisfied apprentice, you will need to study the teachings of *The Message*. You will need to learn how to meditate — in a deep form of meditation that goes beyond the repetition of syllables and phrases and cuts to the core of being a receptor of the truth. You will need to discover how to ask for and receive the great spiritual blessings. In that way, you can obtain the inner peace that the God-Presence alone can bring. This will all be a walk — a slow walk at first — and finally a fulfilling sense of growing and becoming. But the walk — the very act of following — is important. Because *The Message* says we must go beyond merely hearing the words of revelation, we must be willing to do what those words tell us to do.

"Today, as you meditate and write, I'd like to suggest that you think about those paths you can choose to follow to reach your spiritual objectives. What kind of person do you want to be? What kinds of relationships do you want to experience? What things do you most want revealed to you?

"Enjoy the day, too. It's beautiful out there!"

Tim wasted no time leaving the room, and I was right behind him. He was right — as I already knew from my morning amidst the bees and flowers. It was too perfect a day to sit in the meeting room or go back to my cabin. I found myself wishing that Tocayo had an outdoor picnic area or something where we could eat lunch. Right now, I'd settle for a peanut butter and jelly sandwich on plain white bread if I could eat it outside.

The thought of stretching my underworked muscles appealed to me, so I decided to explore the grounds near the entrance to the property. I must have been looking around, drinking in the beautiful surroundings, because I nearly had a head-on collision with Bonnie. She obviously had the same idea I did — don't leave this place without checking out every square inch.

I walked toward the granite boulders that marked the entrance to the Habitat, picked one that looked about as comfortable as a rock can be, and sat down to write.

JOURNAL ENTRY — FRIDAY MORNING — CONTINUED

This is a tough one. I have no idea what I'm looking for, or expecting from my spiritual journey, so I don't know where I want these paths to lead me. I'm actually afraid my journey has led me nowhere. Perhaps I wasn't meant to go anywhere. Perhaps true enlightenment belongs only to a select few.

I've met a few people who appeared to be in touch with the spiritual realm within themselves, but nothing I have tried has worked. In fact, my new interest in spirituality has more or less left me disappointed — disappointed with myself maybe. I feel very much like a spiritual lightweight. I've gone out on a limb for this or that and come up empty. Why can others so successfully get in touch with their spiritual selves through a trip to Sedona or an insight-filled book or a "personal growth" seminar? In some ways, I was actually happier when I thought everything could be answered by money and material things.

I still have spiritual objectives...and I know what

kind of person I want to be. These two things are inseparable, as far as I can determine.

First, I want to have something certain to believe in, so that I can dedicate myself to a higher purpose. After all the dabbling I've done in crystals and tarot cards and centers of energy — all with only limited success — I am willing to look at Tim's notion of the God-Presence to see what's in it for me. It's probably as easy to accept that spiritual power could be centered in an actual being as it is to accept the power of a sacred rock. Easier, probably.

Second, I want the kind of intimacy Tim has been talking about. If "brothers and sisters" who care are part of the God-Presence package, I'm in. All of my relationships have tended toward the superficial and transient. That could be because I was always in them for what I could get out of them. I'm beginning to see that there is something to all the talk at Tocayo about self-centeredness, after all.

Third, I'm tired of searching. I'm tired of thinking that the answer is always around the next corner, always at the end of the next flight, always on the next page of the next book. I want to come to the end of my journey and find something that works for me personally. I want to be a person who is content in his discoveries about life and spirituality.

Finally, I want to discover and embrace a single, clear, definable belief system. I've tried the "assemble your own" approach to my beliefs, and I don't think it's working. Rocks, artifacts, crystals, sacred writings, meditation, astrology, tarot, Eastern religion, Catholicism, Protestantism, Judaism, Islam, reincarnation — all of these things offer certain elements that appeal to me, but none of them seem to be complete and whole in and of themselves. I'm not knocking them — they may have it together more than I know. I just haven't gotten the answers I need out of them. As much as I disdain organized religion, I have to admit that among my friends are Muslims and Jews, Hindus and Catholics, Mormons and Lutherans and Baptists who are content with their beliefs and are living them as best they can. But that's just not where I'm at.

So I guess what I'm saying is if *The Message* has answers for all, or even most, of the questions of my life, I'm willing to be open-minded. But, Tim, or someone else who comes along, is still going to have to show me. I wasn't born in Missouri for nothing.

✦

I closed my journal and sat there in silence, just soaking up the sun. It was getting quite warm, and I had dressed more in keeping with the early morning temperatures. There was just enough time before lunch to stop by the cabin to change into a short-sleeve shirt. But on the way, I remembered I was out of clean clothes. So I changed my course instead — for the dining room.

Several people were gathered outside the closed door. Apparently, the doors weren't opened until the meal chimes sounded. But how would I know? I hadn't been early for anything all week, meals included.

We were all seated, our soup was being served, and Bonnie

still hadn't arrived. I didn't think anything of it because I had skipped meals myself.

About halfway through the main course — some sort of fish that was blackened beyond recognition (but I did enjoy the Cajun seasoning!) — Bonnie showed up looking like absolute crud. She had obviously been crying. Her eyes were red and puffy, and her nose looked like it had been sandpapered. I hate that look. Connie has done that to me more than once.

Bonnie managed a smile that looked somewhat genuine and sat down. "I sure hope she spills her guts tomorrow night," I thought. I was actually looking forward to our last dinner together because we would be able to talk again. I was eager to hear what the others had thought of their week here. Had any of them been struck by the lightning of major insights?

After a dessert of baked apples, I blew out of there for my cabin. I had completed the assignment of the day to the best of my ability, and after my sleepless night, I was fading fast. A nap topped my list of priorities in life.

Unseen Worlds

Chimes, chimes, chimes! Now *there* was a sound I wouldn't miss when I traveled back to the civilized world of burgers and fries and fax machines and cellular phones.

Another two or three hours of sleep would have suited me just fine, but the chimes obviously meant that our afternoon seminar was upon us.

I was still rubbing my eyes when I took my place in row three, second chair from the left. I'm amazed I remembered my Journal in the midst of my groggy stupor.

The guy sitting next to me was doing his usual thing. "The Meditator," I called him. In front of me was a chair that had been empty since the second day. A Tocayo dropout, I decided. As I looked around the room to kill time, it occurred to me that Tim was late. I was relieved to discover that ol' Tim wasn't perfect after all!

All eyes, even my tired ones, were on Tim as he entered the room and walked up to the podium, a little more quickly than usual.

"Sorry I'm late," he began. "I was originally going to continue with my thoughts on the concept of family, because I want you to understand that if you willingly enter a relationship with the God-Presence, Michael will become your true brother. As will many people like him. The riffraff of the world, you might say. And that could be a disturbing barrier to many of you. Because you believe that you are at least one step above Michael and his kind."

I glanced at Michael out of the corner of my eye. He was wearing a classic poker face.

"But, before I came here, I spent time in meditation in communion with God-Presence. As a result, I feel I am not here to talk about family. Instead, I'm going to talk about what each of us are, and what we become when we unite with the God-Presence. I want you to understand that you and I and Michael all come from the same place, but he is heading in a new direction toward a new dimension — a place and time that can be yours. A place and time I already know is mine.

"*The Message* says that all of us have exhibited our flair for self-centeredness, and as a result, we have created a great wall between ourselves and the God-Presence. This wall was of our own choosing and our own building. Our stubbornness and our reliance on ourselves or our empty religions and philosophies keep it firmly in place. But the God-Presence is all about loving and tearing down walls, and turning wrongs into rights and teaching us how to live at peace with each other — without any walls.

"The God-Presence tries to tear down the walls bit by bit, but we constantly and quickly replace the missing pieces, and the wall never goes away. It is only when we do our part — when we quit rebuilding and join in to tear down every inch of that wall — that the God-Presence can step into our lives and transform our self-centeredness and alienation into giving, forgiving, and renewal.

"But don't think for a moment that you can accomplish this entirely on your own. *The Message* says very clearly that *'those who think they can do it on their own end up obsessed with measuring their own moral muscle but never get around to exercising it in real life.'* And obsession with self, it teaches, is a dead end. Attention on the God-Presence *'leads us out into the open, into a spacious, free life.'*

"Many of you have told me in our conferences that you feel you aren't living a free life. I believe that's because you're concentrating on what you can do for yourself, through journeys or mysticism, or following a certain regimen, rather than on what the God-Presence can do for you — as a free, unrestrained gift. You don't earn gifts, dear friends. They're given to you. But you still have to accept them or they do you no good.

"If you really want to experience freedom, all you have to do is turn your face and your heart away from your former motives — your self-centeredness, your envy, your lusts, your greed, all the diseases that infect humanity — and invite the God-Presence to step into your life with a complete set of new motives and new priorities. When you do, all of the old things disappear — the old life is gone and a new life grows in its place. To put it very simply, anyone united with the God-Presence gets a fresh start!

"So many people try to get this fresh start through other people, through the perceptions of mystics and fortunetellers, through following the do's and don'ts of a certain religion, through a new job in a new city, or through a new wife or a new family.

"But all of these things combined cannot satisfy the innermost desire for the God-Presence."

Tim took a deep breath. "It's useless for me to try to explain this in words you will understand. This is not theory. It cannot be learned in a classroom. It cannot be duplicated in a laboratory. You can't think your way into communion with the God-Presence. It's not an intellectual matter. It's an experience, and until you have it, you will never understand it — just as you can't really comprehend an earthquake or a hurricane until you've actually lived through the experience for yourself.

"We won't be having a seminar tonight. Instead, I'll be out by the north garden from now till sunset, and after sunset in my office, to talk with any of you who want to know more about the great gift of the God-Presence. I'll skip dinner if I have to, because it's important to me that any questions you have get the best answers I can possibly give.

"Before I go, I'm going to talk to God-Presence through the Spirit given to me — the one who enables me to do so. You may think this is strange, but it is the way we connect with the God-Presence.

"Great God-Presence, as you have revealed yourself to people of every nation and every race, young and old, rich and poor, so I know you can reveal yourself to the searchers at Tocayo. All they must do is ask, in the stillness of their souls, and you will enter. They will accept your free gift of oneness, by agreeing with you that the old ways must be shunned, and that you must be at the center of each being. We exalt you, creator of new life, purveyor of the eternal and everlasting. We say yes. Yes!"

Well, that was the weirdest thing I'd ever heard! I wasn't all that sure I wanted to meet this oddball in the garden or anywhere else. Did I hear right? Was he talking to a spirit? It reminded me of prayers I used to hear in church as a kid. But not much. This was different. I really think the guy believed he was talking to a real, live being. Maybe he was. Scary thought.

The Night of Becoming

I suppose I could blow a few minutes talking about the lines of people waiting to talk to Tim out by the garden — or the heavily curried, Indian-inspired dish we had for dinner — or my lonely walk in the woodlands — or the raccoons I saw scurrying around the trash dumpster. I could babble on and on about the sunset over the lake. I could provide a vivid description of the aroma of unwashed clothes that had overtaken my cabin, or endless details about the bark chips on the path to my cabin.

But this night was yet to unfold. About twenty minutes before my scheduled time in the meditation room, I stepped out of my cabin into the night air. The sky was alive with the fire of the northern lights. My cabin, the surrounding trees, and the path leading to the main building were lit by the soft pastel light.

What a place and time! I could almost sense a new reality in this night — perhaps the God-Presence was here after all. If that was the case, it certainly wasn't the same God my parents believed in — because *that* one had no more interest in me than I had in him or her.

The countless stars in the darkened sky didn't point to the simplistic answers my parents believed in. Those heavenly lights declared a glory beyond my comprehension!

I recalled all of the other things I'd investigated over the past few years. The guide at Teotihuacán had simplistic answers, too. Sun, moon, nature — I couldn't see all of that working for me. Somehow, others had stumbled upon realities that satisfied their inner spiritual needs. Was I so different that I could not come to peace? Why was I so dissatisfied with my existence?

My life to this point seemed one huge seeking after self-satisfaction. As I walked toward the lodge, I began to list the reality of it in my mind:

My relationships were self-centered — I only thought of myself in every instance.

Even my search for spiritual realities was self-centered. The only reason I sought spiritual answers was because I felt a need inside. I had spent thousands of dollars on tickets, travel accommodations, books, self-help tapes, weekend courses, and even this retreat center. I did it all to feel better, to become fulfilled, and to know that there was a purpose for my self-centered life.

My self-centeredness was what alienated me from making true and lasting friendships. Thinking of myself first was what kept me from enjoying an intimate relationship with Connie. I was always worried about what *I* was getting out of the relationship.

Even my relationship with the kids was messed up. I was doing only those things that would convince other people that I was an ideal dad. Was I just using them?

With every step, I became more dissatisfied with myself. Man, I was a selfish human being! I felt I had no right to even step into the meditation room. It should probably be reserved for those who really need its quietness to heighten their spiritual awareness. It would be a major waste of time for someone like me to spend time there.

It wasn't quite 10:30 when I approached the closed door. I glanced at the sign-up sheet. Tony Somebody-or-Other had logged in for the 9:30 to 10:30 time slot and was no doubt still in there.

I only had to wait a moment. Almost as if on cue, this guy with something I could only describe as a glow on his face emerged from the room. I think I may have had that glow myself once, following a particularly long, rough session of racquetball at the club. But I knew this wasn't a racquetball court.

I had pictured this room as a small, drab, colorless cubicle — no larger than the phone booths in which Superman would change out of his street clothes into his blue tights. But Tocayo continued to surprise me!

When I stepped inside, I discovered a warm, inviting room that resembled a comfortable den in a carefully crafted mansion of another time. It was fairly spacious — about twenty by twenty — with subtle recessed lighting that was accented by strategically placed lamps and reading lights. The bottom portion of the walls was paneled in beautifully grained mahogany; the top part featured a sweeping stucco pattern with carefully spaced vertical wood strips. In one corner was a small mahogany desk that matched the paneling in color and grain. On the opposite side of the room, there was a comfortable-looking sofa.

An object near the center of the room reminded me of a church kneeling bench — the kind that one would use for repentant prayer or taking communion or some other religious rite. Yet there were no religious symbols of any kind in the room. No suns, moons, stars, pyramids, crosses, stars of David, yin-yang circles, or crystals. No statue of a round-bellied Buddha or a prayerful Virgin Mary; no portrait of a bleeding Jesus Christ or Shirley MacLaine in her most recent incarnation.

On the back wall behind the "kneeling bench," there was an intrusive painting that gave me the impression that the artist was a Picasso "wanna-be." It was confusing and disturbing. The painter was *anything* but Picasso. I thought it was out of place here.

On the front wall was a beautiful oil painting signed by an artist named Fred Somers. It pictured a rustic rural scene with tall prairie grasses and a weathered barn. Though somewhat typical, it was still peaceful, restful, beautiful, and expressive. I could almost reach out, touch it, and experience it.

I assumed I was supposed to kneel at the bench, so I did. When I looked behind me, I saw only discord and creative frustration in the abstract art. When I looked ahead, I saw harmony and warmth. The peace that had eluded me over the last few hours was right there in this room — directly in front of me.

For more than twenty minutes, I stared at the painting. The grasses actually gave the illusion of waving in the breeze — and the sense of peace continued to reach into my being. I hoped that this feeling wasn't another illusion.

It was becoming clear to me why this room was booked almost every hour of the day. This was the most energized space at Tocayo. On a small stand next to me was a well-worn paperback book, opened to a particular page. Without closing it and losing that spot, I picked it up, turned it over, and looked at the cover. It was *The Message*.

I looked at the pages that someone before me had been reading, and these words flashed out at me like a brilliant beacon:

"The Word was first,
the Word present to God,
The Word was God,
in readiness for God from day one.
The Life-Light blazed out of the darkness;
the darkness couldn't put it out.
The Life-Light was the real thing;
Every person entering Life
he brings into the Light.
He made them to be their true selves,
their child-of-God selves.
These are the God-begotten,
not blood-begotten,
not flesh-begotten,
not sex-begotten.
The Word became flesh and blood,
and moved into the neighborhood.
We saw the glory with our own eyes,
the one-of-a-kind glory...
like Father, like Son,
Generous inside and out,
true from start to finish."

What was this? The story of the reckless son who returned to his father? Or the story of a reckless father who sent his son far from all his rightful comforts of a celestial palace to rescue a sick and dying world?

Six pages later, the answer stared me in the face. Someone before me had underlined these words, as though they were doing it for me:

"This is how much God loved the world:
He gave his Son, his one and only Son.
And this is why:
so that no one need be destroyed;
by believing in him,
anyone can have a whole and lasting life.
...He came to help,
to put the world right again."

God, how I wanted this! I yearned for a whole life. A lasting life. That's why, bottom line, I was on my spiritual journey. That's why I was at Tocayo. And my search had led me to this room, to this book, and to these exact words!

I had so many questions and so many doubts. But I suddenly grasped who this book was written about! It was Jesus Christ. No doubt about that. And yet...and yet...I still didn't want to have anything to do with him — religious relic who had no real meaning in the last few years of the twentieth century. After all, I was far more enlightened than that.

But this book...this Message...talked about a Jesus Christ I had never heard of before, in words that made him seem so real, so attainable, so relevant. This wasn't the stuffy sixteenth-century language of the church. The writer of this book, through a translator, was speaking directly to me in words I could understand.

"Anyone who drinks the water I give
will never thirst — not ever.
The water I give will be an artesian spring within,
gushing fountains of endless life."

I couldn't believe Jesus Christ had ever said anything like that, but there it was in black and white. I could choose to believe it or not.

I searched my mind for some logic to build my belief on, but I couldn't find any. I wanted this "gushing fountain of endless life," whatever that meant, yet there weren't any logical reasons to trust these words. At least not readily at my command. "Okay, it's up to you, God-Presence, or Jesus, or whoever you are. If you're going to prove yourself to me, you'll have to *make* yourself real."

These questions bubbled to the surface of my mind like volcanic gasses and ignited into a deafening explosion. Suddenly, in this still, silent room, the quiet was shattered! I was sure no one else had heard a sound, but I knew that something I couldn't explain was happening — something almost bizarre. I knew that the presence of God — perhaps what Tim meant by the "God-Presence" — was in the room.

I was so certain of the presence of a spirit-being that it could not have been more real if I had seen Tim walk into the room. This presence and energy was all around me. I experienced awesome terror and profound peace in the same instant.

"God," I said aloud, "this must be God!"

The words rushed out of my mouth. "Please don't be the God I don't believe in, because if you are, I don't want you," I pleaded. "Please don't be the God of empty religion who turns people into robots who don't give a rip about others," I begged. "Please don't be the God of form and routine and liturgy and the Christian Right," I screamed. "If you *are* real, be more real than that!"

I flipped back and forth the pages of the book and read more, devouring the words and feeling them sink deep into my spirit-being.

"*God-light streamed into the world,*

but men and women everywhere ran for the darkness.
Everyone who makes a practice of doing evil,
addicted to denial and illusion,
hates God-light and won't come near it,
fearing a painful exposure.
But anyone working in truth and reality
welcomes God-light so the work can be seen
for the God-work it is."

Were these words talking about me? Was that possible? This was an ancient book, after all.

Was I addicted to denial and illusion? I sure didn't want to admit to that. But my self-centeredness was turning out to be more real than I wanted. And my denial of the existence of a God, or perhaps the God-Presence, was at the core of my belief system.

There had been so much darkness in my life, so much searching, and so little light. But this small room was energized by the God-Presence — one who claimed to be light and truth. All my searching had revealed to me a partial light, but nothing as complete as I saw in this book.

No wonder Tim was so enthused about *The Message*! It was as if he couldn't keep this good news to himself. He had to share it! No matter how diligently I had searched, nothing I had found could measure up to what I was discovering this very moment. The God-Presence was truth, and nothing could be more real to me right now. How could I have missed this? How could my searching have led to so many dead ends?

Instantly, I knew that there was spiritual reality unlike any I had ever experienced — unlike even my accountant had described. I felt loved. I felt accepted. It was like I had come home. I could see that my trip to Tocayo was based on all the wrong motives — they were solely mine and totally selfish.

My mind flashed back many years, to thoughts of Josh and Amy. I could picture them when they were very young. I knew when they wanted something because they'd hug me and tell me they loved me — but I didn't care what their motives were. I was just so happy and content to have them nestled in my arms. I felt that the presence in the room understood my ulterior motives for getting close — but that I was truly loved anyway.

"Are you tired? Worn out?
Burned out on religion?
Come to me.
Get away with me and you'll recover your life.
I'll show you how to take a real rest.
Walk with me and work with me —
watch how I do it.
Learn the unforced rhythms of grace.
I won't lay anything heavy or ill-fitting on you.
Keep company with me,
and you'll learn to live freely and lightly."

I continued reading for more than a half hour — my heart wanted to devour each word and incorporate them into my spirit. Suddenly, with a shout, I said, "These words are truth!"

I was startled by the sound of my own voice and at its conviction. What was I saying? This was the type of stuff that I had learned to reject as a teen, and then more intelligently as an adult. This was part and parcel of the bigotry I had detested in my folks. Their life hadn't been a reality — was I betraying all my years of frustration and exploration? Was I betraying all that I had learned through this last year? I wanted truth, and suddenly it was in my hands — Lord, it was all around me!

"Walk by the light you have
so darkness doesn't destroy you.
If you walk in darkness,
you don't know where you are going.
As you have the light,
believe in the light.
Then the light will be within you,
and shining through your lives.
You'll be children of light."

I could see myself in these words. I had been fumbling around in the dark, groping for this, tugging at that, hoping for some "light" that made sense. And here it was! I could become a child of light.

Everything I read was so alive and so powerful, I wanted to not only understand it, I wanted it to be part of my life.

Again I said aloud, almost with a shout, "These words are truth, and I would die for them!"

"WHAT? Calm down, Jeff! I hadn't even been willing to die for my wife just a few days ago — what am I saying? What is happening to me?"

As I stopped to think, the reality became even clearer. With determination I repeated, "These words are truth, and I would die for them."

In an instant, the presence of God that was in the room rushed inside of me! There are no words to describe a spiritual experience of this magnitude. It was nothing but supernatural. The very presence and person of God was invading my whole being. I wanted to cry and laugh at the same time.

I had come to this room to meditate, and I had found the door to spiritual reality. It had been the very door that I had rejected and turned away from so many times. And now, tonight, all alone, I was opening it.

For more than an hour I continued to read, skipping around the book searching for words that others had underlined. I found something that reminded me of what Tim had said:

"Now we look inside, and what we see is
that anyone united with the Messiah
gets a fresh start, is created new.
The old life is gone; a new life burgeons!
Look at it! All this comes from the God
who settled the relationship between us and him,
and then called us to settle
our relationships with each other."

This was the answer to alienation. This was it! I wanted to settle my relationships with God and with my wife and kids and the people in my world.

All the other paths to truth that I had followed didn't seem to offer resolution to my inner conflicts. But the peace that had been in the room now filled my being.

"I am the world's Light,"
...this God-Presence says...
"No one who follows me
stumbles around in the darkness.
I provide plenty of light to live in.
I am the Road,
also the Truth,
also the Life.
No one gets to the Father apart from me."

This was wild! The God of heaven who walked on earth, this Jesus Christ, claimed to be the only path back home to the Father.

And I, in the middle of my doubts, believed him. I had nothing to lose.

The more I read, the more I wanted to read.

"If our Message is obscure to anyone,
it's not because we're holding back in any way.
No, it's because these other people are looking
or going the wrong way
and refuse to give it serious attention.
All they have eyes for
is the fashionable god of darkness.
They think he can give them what they want,
and that they won't have to bother
believing a truth they can't see.
They're stone-blind to the dayspring brightness
of the Message that shines with Christ,
who gives us the best picture of God we'll ever get."

I found myself talking to God-Presence — not visible, but so present and so real. I poured out the frustrations that had been nagging at my inner being — the aspirations that I had for my kids, the uncertainties about my relationship with Connie, my discontent with my dead-end job, and the house payments that left us poor every month. And my feelings that through all of this I had never measured up to anything useful or successful.

In that moment, I felt the God-Presence saying, "I am here for you; I am with you. You are loved more than you know. You are more valuable than you can imagine. I am throwing a wonderful celestine party in your honor, because you have come home, my son!"

It wasn't that I actually heard anyone speak these words. It was more of an inner voice. I couldn't explain it. I sure hoped Tim could. He'd have his chance in our last conference tomorrow!

I turned to the last few pages of *The Message*. It was a "revelation" of some sort. I was ready to dig in to find out what it said when I heard the sound of someone outside the door. There was a gentle knock. I looked at my watch — it was 7:00 A.M. I couldn't believe it! I had been there for over eight hours, reading, thinking, talking with someone I couldn't even see, yet someone I knew was there with me.

My time was up, that was for sure! I rose to my feet and walked over to the door at about the same time it was opened by a visitor. It was Bonnie-of-Hollywood. "Jeff!" she exclaimed, breaking the vow of silence we had all observed so carefully. "Jeff, what has happened to you?"

Could she really see something different about me? Was it evident on my face, or was it some kind of aura?

"Jeff, you look so different. You look at peace. You're even radiant! What happened?"

I tried to speak, but the words were caught in my throat. I didn't want to sound stupid. And right at that moment, I knew that would be easy.

"What is it, Jeff?" she urged.

I decided I had to tell her, no matter how crazy it sounded.

"I...I...m-met the God-Presence," I stammered. "He was here. He's real. And...and...get this...he's Jesus Christ!"

She took my hand. Gently. Not in any kind of sexual way. "I know. I've met him, too. I don't think I'd even be alive if he wasn't alive."

"When did you meet him?" I wanted to know.

"Shhh!" she responded. "We're not supposed to be talking, remember? I'll tell you at dinner tonight."

Tonight?! I forgot. It was the morning of my last full day at Tocayo. My last conference with Tim. The last seminars. And I hadn't slept the entire night. Again. How was I going to make it through the day?

Bonnie walked over to the small bench and got down on her knees. She immediately picked up *The Message* and started to read.

I took that as a hint and left, quietly closing the door behind me. There was plenty of time for a shave and shower before breakfast, but not enough extra time for even a short nap.

On the path to my cabin, I thought about my long night in the meditation room. Did everyone who came to the Habitat meet the God-Presence in that room? As silly as the question sounded to me, I wondered, "Is that where the God-Presence lives?" I threw out *that* thought about as quickly as it had occurred to me.

My mind wandered throughout all of heaven and earth as I rinsed the pungent dandruff shampoo out of my hair. What would Tim think about my experiences? Had Michael discovered the same things in his prison cell that I stumbled on in the meditation room? Do the people sitting in churches on Saturday or Sunday even have a clue what this is all about? Or do they only care how good they look, or how the things they say sound in conversations with others of their kind?

I was the last to take my place for breakfast, but that didn't matter. I've always managed to eat enough to stay alive, even when I haven't allowed adequate time for the task. I caught Bonnie's eyes as I unfolded my napkin. Her whole face was a smile! It comforted me.

I looked into the faces of the others. I could tell we were all looking forward to talking to each other at dinner, although some of them looked as though they had less to say than others.

My conference with Tim wasn't until 10:30. We had a seminar at 3:30, and another after dinner that night. That left lots of time to write in my journal — and I had lots to write!

After breakfast, I walked down to the lake. Someone had beat me to the dock, so I sat on a fallen tree near the shoreline. I wondered what did it in. Lightning maybe. Or the wind. Or old age.

I opened my journal and started to write.

JOURNAL ENTRY — MY LAST FULL DAY AT TOCAYO
Last night was quite the night.

Well, that was it. That was all I wrote. All week long, I'd filled the pages of my journal with nothing but my "attitude." Then, the biggest thing happened to me that I've ever experienced in my life, and I had nothing to write. I can't believe myself sometimes. Ten pages on Mexico, then this. Geez!

I sat for a minute, and then I had an idea. "God-Presence, are you here with me right now?" I asked in a hushed voice.

There was no way I could ever prove it to anyone, but I was sure he was there with me. So I talked to him. I told him about all the thoughts I had written in my journal since coming to Tocayo Habitat. I told him about my disillusionment — how every pursuit in my life had resulted in a feeling of emptiness. Teotihuacán had been a huge letdown. Sedona was beautiful but not enlightening, at least in my case. My desire for material things had left me feeling vacant inside. And, of course, my marriage had more downs than ups. Whoever wrote the wedding vows that include the phrase "for better or worse" sure knew what they were talking about.

I hoped with all my heart and soul that my discovery of the God-Presence wouldn't eventually end in disappointment and crush my latest hope that there *were* spiritual realities I could depend on. So I told him he had to be very real to me, so that I wouldn't doubt and move on to the next thing.

The thought — or rather the frustration — that kept running through my mind was that, indeed, the God-Presence Tim had been talking about and the Jesus Christ I had heard about as a kid were one and the same. It had been easy to discard Jesus; it would be tough to accept him as reality.

JOURNAL ENTRY — SATURDAY MORNING — ANOTHER TRY AT IT

The more I've become aware of my spiritual side, the more I've been willing to accept mysterious beliefs as possible truths.

Take ghosts, or spirits, or whatever you want to call them. There must be another dimension where spirit-beings exist...where we can't see them. As dumb as it probably sounds to the "truly enlightened" people of the world, movies like *Ghost* and *Always* have had a genuine impact on me. It could be mostly because I really want to believe in a life hereafter.

Or how about angels? Even people who have no time for God or Christ believe in these invisible, helpful "heavenly hosts." I remember hearing about angels way back in Sunday school. They zapped into sudden view and announced the birth of Jesus to some poor, smelly shepherds. At least that's how I recall the story; I'll have to check.

I believe a lot of what the Asian and Middle Eastern religions teach, too. They have many truths to share, based on the teachings of other prophets and teachers.

My latest thing has been "centers of energy" — vortexes (or is it vorteces?) where the cosmic powers of the universe come together and do whatever it is they do. I've never figured out what that is, but millions of people believe it, so there must be something to it.

Why, then, do I have such a problem with Jesus Christ? After all, he must have played some sort of pivotal role in human history. We've based our calendars on him for practically two thousand years. If he were nothing — if he didn't count for anything significant — why does so much of the Western world say "In the year of our Lord such-and-such"? Why not "In the year of Aristotle," or the year of Socrates or Plato or Leonardo da Vinci? Surely they were great men. And what about women? History is rich with women of greatness. Who knows? Maybe in two thousand years, people will be saying "In the year of Mother Theresa." Oops! I almost forgot. She's in the "Jesus Believers" column, too.

Most of the educated people I've known over the years will believe in a lot of things before they'll believe in Jesus Christ. All of a sudden, I'm not sure why that is. Of course, I'm not sure why people are Democrats or Republicans, either.

The problem might be that, as near as I can tell, he

asks for commitment and he expects change. And we don't like those words. I'm eager to get my own copy of *The Message* and find out what it really says. Does it offer revelations about the "God-Presence" that we've never heard before? It must, because I don't ever remember hearing any of what I read last night. It all seemed so distanced from "religion."

Maybe it's a case of what we've done to Jesus over the years. We've pressed him into our mold. Made him fit our beliefs, our desires, or our need for ritual. We've wimped him out. We've painted him in white robes with a glowing red heart bursting out of his chest and a goofy halo over his head. But *The Message* tells of a Jesus with guts, with feelings, and with the most incredible, unbelievable love I've ever read about. Or dreamed existed.

Well, Mr. Jesus, if you can be that real in the pages of a book, I guess you can be that real to me. There were sure no doubts in my mind last night.

Even after I closed my journal, using my pen as a bookmark, my mind continued to race along. If there were people in great cathedrals and huge churches who could comprehend all this, they certainly didn't give the impression that it made much of a difference to them. I was confident I could do without them and their pious ways, and their sanctuaries filled with statues and prayer books and stained-glass windows. And, for sure, their collection plates. Money talks, even in church.

All I cared about at that moment was talking to Tim. I wanted

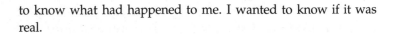
to know what had happened to me. I wanted to know if it was real.

The Commitment

I walked toward Tim's office with a little more excitement than I had displayed on previous days. In my eagerness to meet with him, I arrived at his office almost a half hour before my scheduled time. His door was closed, so I knew, or at least assumed, that someone else was in there with him.

The reasonable and appropriate thing to do, I thought, was to pace. I walked down to the dining room, over to the meeting room, past the library, and back to Tim's office. The door was still closed. I should have expected that, since only three minutes had elapsed. So I walked past the library, over to the meeting room, and back from the dining room. Another three minutes. Door still closed. I appeared to have gotten this down to a science.

A fresh idea crossed my mind. "On the next pass, I'll stop in the library. Brilliant, Jeff!" So off I went. The library door was closed, but it didn't matter — unlike Tim's office and the meditation room, the library had been open to anyone, anytime, all throughout the retreat.

When I walked in, I discovered the library already had an

occupant. Michael was seated at the small desk, deeply engrossed in a very thick book. My first impulse was to say, "Excuse me," leave, and resume pacing. But I decided to stay.

Michael set aside his book, turned in his chair, and said, "Morning, Jeff." The rules about talking must relax on the last day, I decided, so I responded, "How're you doing, Michael?"

"Great! How's the retreat going for you?"

"I had an interesting night..."

"I can tell that," he said.

"What do you mean? How can you tell that?"

"Jeff, when something has happened to someone, they can sort of tell when it's happened to someone else."

I was taken by surprise. "You mean you can tell when someone has experienced the God-Presence, just by looking at them?"

"Absolutely. But there was no way I could see this in another person until it had happened to me. It's what I call 'family resemblance.' We inherit certain visible and spiritual characteristics from our Father, the Father of the God-Presence. We become the brothers and sisters of the God-Presence, and his character, personality, and countenance are evident in all of us."

"So," I asked, "you can look around at all the people here and tell by their appearance which ones know the God-Presence and which ones don't?"

"Yes, for the most part. But it's not only appearance. It's attitude, spirit, and heart. It's the total person — innermost and outermost."

I decided to put him to the test. "Okay, how about John, the doctor who sits at my table?"

Michael didn't even hesitate. "Searching, arrogant, lonely,

confused, but in so much pain he doesn't know why he's all these things. He really needs the God-Presence in his life to heal the pain and help him find all that he's looking for."

"How about Bonnie?"

Again, no hesitation. "Oh, she knows the God-Presence, all right. But there is something she has not yet resolved. Some hurt in her past. I don't know what it is, but it's there. I tried to talk to her the other day, but she wouldn't let it out. It's very deep inside her."

I was beginning to see Michael in a new light. He was more than just an ex-con who had "found God."

"Michael, have you really been able to recover from your past?" My question was sincere; I genuinely wanted to know.

"I know I will always have to live with the scars of the terrible thing I did. But the God-Presence has promised me that I am forgiven, and that what I did is forever removed from my life and his memory. So I have become a new person with a fresh start. Because I know my future, I no longer have to live in the past. But if I could die to give that woman life again, I would. I'd do anything."

I understood what he was saying. "We can never go back, can we, Michael?"

"No," he said, looking me straight in the eye. "But with the God-Presence, we can go forward."

With that, Michael put away his book, touched me on the shoulder in passing, said "See you later, Jeff," and quietly walked out. I sat there for a few minutes and thought about the conversation, until it finally occurred to me that if I didn't get moving, I'd miss my conference with Tim.

The door to Tim's office was open when I got there, but he was nowhere to be seen. I decided to walk in and settle into the chair next to his desk. His copy of *The Message* was sitting on the edge of the desk, so I picked it up, started reading, and was thoroughly engrossed by the time he walked in.

"Well, you've certainly had some significant experiences since I last met with you," Tim observed.

"You've got to be kidding," I said. "You're the second person to say that in the last ten minutes. Did Michael talk to you?"

"No. I actually noticed the new spirit within you at breakfast. The God-Presence provides clear evidence of his being."

"Michael called it 'family resemblance,' " I offered.

"That's a good way to put it," Tim said. "I guess I never looked at it that way before."

I hesitated, not knowing where to begin. "I'm not sure what happened to me last night. It was unlike anything I've ever experienced. All the other things I've done — my travels, the meditation, the books I've read — all this seems really insignificant. It was like scales fell from my eyes and I could see into the spiritual world for the first time. If the God-Presence isn't real, what happened to me in that room has to be the grandest hallucination anyone has ever had."

Tim laughed. "You certainly have an interesting way with words. But I know exactly what happened to you, no matter how you describe it."

"Is this real?" I asked. "Is my experience valid?"

"Do you want it to be?"

"Why? Are you telling me that it really could all be a state of mind, but that if I want it bad enough, it's real?"

Tim smiled. "No, I'm telling you that you'll never be able to submit your experience to a laboratory test. You'll never be able to say 'I have seen the God-Presence, therefore I know.' Every step you take from this day forward will be based on that old concept of faith."

I was incredulous. "Faith? That's it? That's all you have to offer? People don't accept things by faith anymore." Even as I was speaking, I knew that I clung on to my own beliefs in ghosts and angels and whatever. I was hoping Tim had an answer that would sweep away my remaining doubts about the God-Presence.

"Oh, no? Do you think people who believe in reincarnation can prove it? Can they show you their first, second, and third birth certificates? They hold that belief inside, they have some deja-vu-type memories, and that's about it. Do you think that anyone can prove that there's power in rock formations, or that the sun, moon, and stars control human destiny? How many famous astrologers have had their predictions go up in smoke? Yet many people follow their horoscopes with tremendous dedication. People who believe in anything they can't see or hear or touch do so by faith. If any single belief system could be scientifically proven beyond all doubt, all of us would follow that belief without question. The entire human race would get in line with it.

"I don't understand how a 747 can fly, Jeff, but I'll board one without any hesitation. I don't question the fact that the air, which I can't even see, can support the weight of a 400-ton mass of metal, wires, cables, bolts, rivets, and people. I know it has something to do with the forces of lift and gravity, and thrust and drag. I know all of it can be proven scientifically, but I still don't really understand it.

"Jeff, if we had to understand everything we accept, we wouldn't accept much of anything. We'd be immobilized by fear and doubt."

At that moment, the Dunker came to mind. As an accountant, he was always interested in the bottom line. He accepted only those things that added up in black and white. The numbers. Not imaginary numbers; the real ones. I wondered why he was so open to *The Celestine Prophecy*, the Sedona experience, and other mystical beliefs. It must be faith.

"I guess you're right," I finally admitted. "But isn't all this God-Presence stuff just repackaged Christianity?"

Tim paused. I had good reason to think that I may have gotten him with this one. "No," he began, "what most people consider to be Christianity is what you said you've experienced in the past. It's church. It's form and ritual. It's a place, and the people in that place. The hypocrites, the doubters, the backbiters. It's the guilt and the shame. But real Christianity is a relationship, and nothing more than that. It's what happens in your soul when the God-Presence becomes your constant companion. Your best friend. It's what happens when you experience a deep bond with your brothers and sisters in your new family. It's what happens when you die to yourself — when you turn your back on your self-centered ways — and embrace the Light."

I had countless questions. Some of them had been answered through my experiences in the meditation room. Others were expressions of my deepest doubts. "How do we know that the God-Presence is the Light? The only Light?"

"You *can't* know," Tim answered, "until the Light shines into your life. But when you agree to become open to the God-Presence, the Light shines deep within your soul and illuminates the darkness. When that happens, you will know for sure, and despite the doubts that others throw your way, nothing will dispel the truth from you."

I sat there, puzzled by his explanation, but still hanging on every word. This one day — my last day at Tocayo — I wished my conference with Tim could go on for another hour or two. I had questions. He had answers. Not all of them, but some. I was willing to listen, to sort them out, to pick and choose what I thought would work for me.

But my time was up. I knew someone else was waiting at the door.

"See you later, Jeff," Tim said as he got up from his chair.

"Yeah, see you later, Tim. I hope we have another chance to talk before it's time to leave."

"We will."

When I opened the door, the Invisible Woman was standing there, staring at nothing in particular. She slipped behind me and into Tim's office as invisibly as she could and closed the door behind her. I wondered if there was any chance I'd know more about her when I left than I did when we first got here. Probably not.

On the way back to my cabin, I ran into Doctor John. He was so somber; he didn't crack even a hint of a smile. "Nice seeing you, too," I thought to myself in my most sarcastic tone-of-mind.

When I stepped inside, I was overcome by a presence I could barely describe. No, it wasn't the God-Presence. It was my overripe unwashed clothing. A week's worth of sun and sweat. And laundry. The passing hours had not erased the familiar aroma that had confronted me earlier. So I opened the window as wide as I could and half wished I could punch a large hole in the wall to allow for some cross-ventilation.

Too exhausted from my long night to write, walk, or think, I fluffed up my pillow and closed my eyes. The next thing I knew, the chimes were sounding. That meant lunch, but I didn't care. In fact, I was kind of upset that my nap had been interrupted. So I scrunched my pillow into an entirely new shape and invited sleep to again surround me.

At precisely 3:25 P.M., the chimes sounded again. This time my eyes opened willingly, and I decided I was alert enough to attend the 3:30 seminar. I also decided I could survive without my fragrant socks, so I took them off and slipped into my Nikes. I didn't even care if anyone noticed. I was beginning to feel like a free man.

A brief "pit stop" resulted in my late arrival in the meeting room. I thought everyone might be staring at me, but again, I didn't particularly care. I hadn't done this on purpose; nature had simply placed a call I had to return.

Tim had already begun and was saying something about children.

"Remember when you were a young child? You would do something that made you proud...a trick or a tumble or a riddle or a great catch...and you'd say to anyone nearby, 'Look at me.'

"Often, the adults — your parents or your teacher or whoever else was with you — would ignore you and continue with what they were doing.

"So you'd say again, 'Hey, SOMEBODY, look at me.' You didn't even care who looked. You just wanted attention.

"Well, friends, that's the way we all are. We never really grow up. We want attention...recognition...acceptance. And that's what the God-Presence offers us.

"First, he gave us the attention we wanted and needed so desperately by living among us. No other god of any religion has ever done that for us. He walked with us, experienced our pain, and died alongside us. He participated in the sights, smells, and flavor of the human experience. Because of his utter love for us, he became a part of us enough to know what we were going through. But because the God-Presence is actually God, he has the power to draw us out of our misery and into relationship with him.

"Second, he gave us the opportunity for a new life. He transcended his death and showed the way to a new form of existence in a new reality so far beyond our earthly experience. We could be free of the bonds of our limited physical world by embracing his truth and turning away from the self-centeredness that enslaves us. This involves a conscious decision. It's a simple cycle. Accept the reality of the God-Presence, reject the tyranny of selfishness, and embrace the changes that this new life brings.

"Finally, he gave us everything we need to live all of this as reality. I call them the 'keys to the kingdom.' These keys unlock the doors that guard eternal insights from those who don't know him. Yet these keys are available to anyone who does have a relationship with him, no matter how new that relationship may be.

"These keys are the words he spoke to us, the thoughts we transmit to him, and the thoughts he places within our hearts.

"We discover his words by reading the ancient manuscript that has been passed down through the ages. Its most recent translation is what we call *The Message*.

"We transmit our thoughts to him through the mystery that some call prayer. But prayer is not what you may think it is. It's not the repetition of a few words and phrases. It's not a 'mantra.' It's real, heartfelt communication from the gut. From the deepest part of you. You may cry, and despair, and almost bleed from within when you truly pray. You may even run out of words, and shut up and listen. That's what is really meant by the word 'meditation.' We stop. We wait. We open our hearts, minds, and souls to deeper insights.

"That's when the God-Presence is able to place thoughts within us. When we are quiet. When we aren't consumed with saying everything we think.

"That's why we ask you to pledge to remain silent for your week at Tocayo. There's no better way to hear what the God-Presence wants to say to you. There's no better way to meet him, know him, and hear him speak. One of the most ancient and long-revered religions on earth — Judaism — teaches this profound truth: 'Be still, and know that I am God.'

"Some of you have really stopped to listen this week. That's great! You're on a new journey that will lead you into deeper truths and more profound realities. My only thoughts for you as you leave Tocayo are these: continue to discover his words in *The Message*, communicate with him anytime you sense that you should, and take time to quiet your soul in his presence. Once you meet the God-Presence, he has promised he will never leave you. He will never, never turn his back on you and leave you alone again."

I had never heard such intensity in anyone's voice in my life. Tim was speaking with a fervor that I'm sure even Abraham Lincoln would have envied at Gettysburg. I hoped I wasn't somehow being duped by a slick, professional conman, but my experiences here allowed little room for that thought to grow.

Tim stepped off the platform and walked down the center aisle. "At dinner tonight," he said, "I'll be spending some time with you at your tables. I want to know what you've thought of your week here. Tell me what we can do to better help those who follow you."

As I got up to leave, Bonnie captured my eyes from across the room. I wasn't exactly sure, but I thought I saw her mouth the words, "See you at dinner." I nodded in response.

When I stepped outside the lodge, it was as if I could hear the trails of Tocayo calling me to pay them one last visit. But I ignored them. I had a few thoughts that I wanted to commit to my journal, so I went back to my cabin and placed my chair on the west side, facing the afternoon sun.

JOURNAL ENTRY — SATURDAY AFTERNOON

Who is this God-Presence? Who is Jesus Christ? In our society, his name is as overused and as meaningless as I could ever imagine.

Every time I go to a movie or watch cable TV or attend a meeting at the office, I hear "Jesus Christ! Jesus Christ! Jesus Christ!" Sometimes it's almost every other word. There's an occasional "Holy Moses" thrown in for variety, but you never hear "Richard Nixon" or "Jimmy Carter" or "Thomas Edison." Who was it who decided that if you were shocked or upset or irritated or surprised, the proper response was "Jesus Christ"? That just might demonstrate how important he is. But if I were Jesus Christ, I'd be pretty ticked that I meant nothing more to most people than two words to exclaim when life startles them.

Right now, I want to say "Jesus Christ." But I don't want to say it as an expression of profanity. I want to say it as part of a sentence: "Jesus Christ, if you are the God-Presence of *The Message*, I want to know you. I want to rebuild my relationships with your help. I want to live beyond this short earthly life we've all been given."

All of a sudden, I knew what Tim meant when he said, "You will never know until you know." My experiences the previous night, coupled with my experiences in that moment, were all I needed to know.

No one has to believe a word I say about all of this. It doesn't matter. Because I know.

The Last Supper

If I had brought my tux to Tocayo, I would have wanted to wear it to dinner that last night. And secretly, I hoped there would be balloons on every table, a live band, and one of those revolving mirror balls suspended from the ceiling that made sparkles appear everywhere when spotlights shone on them. I wanted to party. I was in the mood to celebrate.

But, no tux, sad to say. And as I knew so well, no clean clothes either. I gave all of my shirts the "nose test," to determine which one was least likely to be noticed by the others at my table. I picked the one that looked like the kind they sell to tourists in Mexico. Actually, that's where I got it. (I have this habit of buying whatever styles the locals are selling, and then wearing them with pride back home.)

It was at least an hour until dinner, so I decided to start packing my things. We wouldn't be leaving until the next morning, but that didn't matter. I was anxious to get home to Connie and the kids — to love them and hug them, and learn to give to them instead of taking from them all the time. It was an exciting prospect!

I'd been counting the hours to that dinner all day. I wanted to know what kinds of experiences everyone else had felt and touched and tasted. I felt like a teenager, eager to share my own experiences but afraid of what everyone else would think. Then again, last night may have been the most transforming event in my life, and I was more than willing to talk.

When we were all seated at our table, someone suggested that we reintroduce ourselves; a great idea, in light of the fact that I didn't even know the Invisible Woman's name. It turned out to be Danielle.

We engaged in trivial conversation throughout the salad course. Everyone agreed that, for the most part, we had enjoyed wonderful weather all week. Someone commented on spotting a fox, and I brought up the deer I had seen at the edge of the woods.

Then, without so much as a warning, Mary Beth decided to spill her guts — again. It didn't take a Rhodes Scholar to determine that we'd all be doing this before the night was over.

"I came here because I'd found my expectations of life hadn't been fulfilled," Mary Beth began. "That's mostly because of my marriage, as you know. I met my husband through one of those dating clubs, and we got married just four months after we first went out. He is quite a bit older, but that didn't matter to me. I thought he offered security and stability, but each passing year seemed to bring increasing unhappiness. He paid so little attention to me. I never felt affection of any kind. Not even a simple touch.

"So I poured all my energy into our only child, my son Dylan. Then one day, he was off to school and my daily existence suddenly got even more lonely.

"My husband didn't want me to work, so that way of dealing with my loneliness was out of the question. All he cared about was that his shirts were pressed perfectly, and his gourmet meals were ready for him at precisely 6:30, just after his 'come down' gin and tonic.

"I became his little 'show piece.' He took me to business functions and I was supposed to look sexy in my strapless dress and say as little as possible.

"With plenty of free time on my hands, my life became one of binges. Binges on prescription drugs, binges on food, shopping binges, and binges on romance novels. I craved those imaginary romantic substitutes for my terrible excuse of a marriage. My binge on romance novels, just like the others, was a way of medicating my hurt. In the past couple of years, it's been binges on New Age materials and experiences. I've been using all these things to kill the pain inside me.

"I was told that Tocayo was the ultimate New Age experience, one that would help me forget, or maybe recover from, the pain and alienation I was feeling in my life. When Tim began talking about alienation, I found myself blushing — it was like he had read my mind and was talking only about my life. This week has given me new insights on what I have to do to break the chain of alienation in my life. I don't know if I can accept the idea that I can only break the alienation through God-Presence. That seems to be what Tim has been saying, but I want to go back home and give myself another chance at finding the answer through meditation."

Doctor John cracked a wry smile. "Maybe meditation will be your next binge," he said sarcastically.

"That's hardly fair, Doc," I said. "Can't you see this is a serious issue for her? She's genuinely looking for answers."

"Well, that may be," he replied, "but she's certainly not going to find them here, or back home in meditation, either. All of life is nothing more than a collection of circumstances over which we have no control. Some are good, some are bad, but they just happen. You can't change them."

"Oh, yes you can!" It was the congresswoman. "I've started changing mine, right here at the Habitat."

This really interested me, and I could tell by the looks of most of the other faces that they, too, were eager for the whole story.

"My career in public service has always been my life. It has taken precedence over my marriage and over my children. I've always believed that this was the right approach — that I had my values in perspective. I was giving myself to a cause much larger than myself and my family. I was so proud to be living out the kinds of things that my dad had wanted to do...and, in some respects, expected from his eldest daughter.

"One day just this last April, I became keenly aware that I wasn't happy, that I wasn't fulfilled. My life had been very 'me-centered.' I had achieved my dreams and had met my father's expectations. I had my beautiful home within the beltway and a seat on the hill. But with each successive term in Congress, I felt more like a pawn of the political system than someone who could truly make a difference.

"My marriage was only minimally functional, and my married daughter was treating me like cancer. She didn't even think me fit enough as a grandmother to spend time with her children.

"Then, the justice department began its investigation of some of the activities of my campaign staff during the last election. I never approved of what they were doing, but I never stopped them, either.

"So there I was. I'd made a mess of the real important relationships and accomplishments of life. One of my colleagues on the hill recommended that I attend a retreat at Tocayo. I thought it was going to be a good time of reflection and rest, but it became a time of introspection. It's been a frightening week." She paused for a moment and took a sip of water.

"So that's it?" asked John. He looked around the table. "Next!"

The congresswoman laughed despite her serious tone. "John, I'm nowhere *near* finished. I'm a politician, remember?"

"Please continue," Mary Beth said as she flashed a glaring look at John.

The congresswoman took a deep breath and picked up where she had left off. "I was really hit by what Tim talked about in terms of alienation. That to me was the most important insight — I had become alienated from all of the people who meant the most to me. All of the new friends I had made through the networking in my political career couldn't make up for the relationships I'd walked over — my marriage, my children, and my extended family. I was alienated from the people I wanted to spend the rest of my life with.

"As I was thinking and writing this week, I remembered back to a time during my freshman year in college when I had a very strong faith in the one Tim calls the God-Presence. I had become part of a group of students on campus who showed me that I was accepted and loved by God.

"All of my life prior to that had been one big performance — any acceptance that I felt was a result of the things I had accomplished. Suddenly I was face-to-face, so to speak, with a God who didn't care one bit about what I'd achieved — he loved me because I was Jeannette. He knew my name, he knew my

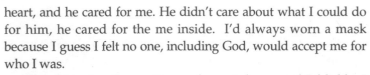

heart, and he cared for me. He didn't care about what I could do for him, he cared for the me inside. I'd always worn a mask because I guess I felt no one, including God, would accept me for who I was.

"For a couple of years the mask went down, and I felt like I was completely accepted by God. But then school politics and my study for a law career crowded out those voices. During my junior year in college, and then throughout law school, I found the masks were once again necessary, and that a relentless drive to get ahead was the only way I would make a name for myself in my chosen career.

"Twenty-four years of a law practice and politics, a stifled marriage, and a lot of damaged relationships had to go under the bridge before I could see that I again needed to feel accepted by God.

"That's what has happened this week. Amazingly, I'm back to where I was as a freshman in college, except that I have a lot of fences to mend. I'm looking forward to starting over in my relationships. I broke the retreat rules and called my daughter yesterday and told her what a mess I had made of our relationship. I asked her to forgive me, and to give me a chance to get to know her.

"I was the most surprised grandma at Tocayo when she cried and said yes — I think I'm going to enjoy getting to know my daughter. Perhaps I'll even have a chance with my grandchild and with my son and his wife. This has been a great week! It's refocused the rest of my life!"

She looked at John and smiled. "You can relax now. I'm finished."

Bonnie glanced around the table, then said, "I think I'm going to need to go last. Anyone else have anything to say?"

"I do," said Danielle.

"Wow," I thought to myself, "maybe we'll all get to know the Invisible Woman after all."

Danielle began slowly, as if she was having second thoughts about sharing her observations on the week.

"I came here not sure I even wanted to go on living. I'm leaving tomorrow with more peace than I've ever known in my life. I've started on the road to healing. It may be a long road, but at least I'm on it."

She started to cry. Bonnie squeezed her hand, as if to comfort and encourage her.

In a couple of minutes, she regained her composure and continued. "I'm here because a friend at work knew I desperately needed a 'time out' and gave me the money to come. I've been barely making ends meet since my boyfriend left me, so I couldn't have come here without her help.

"I was married when I was sixteen — I never even got to finish high school. I was pregnant, and in my family, if you're pregnant, you do the 'right thing.' You get married. No 'quick-fix' abortions in my family history.

"The baby was barely six months old when I got pregnant again. My husband got a job at a grocery store, working in the freezers at night. I took care of babies day and night.

"He started to yell and scream about the diapers and the crying and his crummy job. One night he went to work and never came back. He moved in with some girl who didn't have kids and he filed for divorce two days later.

"There I was, all alone with two babies who needed me for everything, and no job and no money. I moved home with my parents for a while, but that really stressed me out. They were always criticizing the way I was raising my kids. To get away from them and the kids, I'd go to this little bar on the interstate. I met a guy there who was really nice to me, and before long we decided to live together. I would have done anything to get away from my parents.

"I found a neighbor who did day care cheap, so I got a job in the cafeteria at a paper mill. I barely made more than what day care cost, but it was a job and I was proud of it.

"Well, Tom, the guy I was living with, turned out to be the devil himself. After work, he would hang out at the bar where we met, and some nights come home after midnight, stinking drunk. I told him I needed him at home to help with the kids, but that just drove him away.

"One night he came home at two in the morning, and I started yelling at him. He didn't yell back. He started hitting me."

Danielle's voice started to crack with emotion. She wiped away the tears that were welling up in her eyes and continued.

"He hit me harder and harder. I fell to the floor and he kicked me in the stomach. He told me never to yell at him again, then he left.

"I cried myself to sleep that night. The pain was unbelievable — not only the pain from his hitting me, but the pain in my heart. The next morning, I looked in the mirror and got sick to my stomach. I called work to say that I was in an accident and couldn't come in, then I called my dad. He came right over.

"When he got to my apartment, he took one look at me and said, "I'm going to kill the lousy slug." He left and came back at dinnertime. He said he was going to stay with me that night.

"About 11:30, Tom came home, drunker than ever. When he

walked in, my dad pulled a gun from his pocket, put it right up to Tom's forehead, and said, 'If you ever come near my daughter again, you're going to have to scrape your brains off the wall.'

"That was the last we ever saw of Tom. Someone told me he moved to Oklahoma. Good riddance!

"But the next thing I knew, the people from the child welfare department were at my door. They said I was an unfit mother. I tried to keep my kids, but they went to court and took them away from me. They're both in foster homes. Two different ones. They're not even together."

"That's awful," Mary Beth exclaimed.

The rest of us nodded, too stunned to speak.

Danielle had one more thing to say, and she said it so eloquently I'll remember it as long as I walk this planet. "I didn't even know what the word 'alienation' meant when I got here. But I know I've experienced it worse than anyone in this place. If ever there was someone who needed the comfort and love and peace of the God-Presence, it's me. And I discovered him this week. I know, like Tim said, that all the old things are gone forever, and my new life is beginning!"

Doctor John sat there dumbfounded. "I didn't get a thing out of this week," he said. "Nothing. But I'm really happy for all of you. You think that somehow you've gotten a new start here. That things are going to be rosy from now on. That you can meditate, and pray, and read *The Message*, and your rotten lives and sour relationships will somehow turn around.

"Well, I think you've been duped by a slick retreat leader and a book filled with myths. Where is your God-Presence when a child is on his deathbed in a hospital? Where is this Jesus Christ when an entire family is slaughtered in some African country?

Who is the god of famine? What kind of god would create people who hate each other on the basis of their color or their accent?"

Tim had overheard a part of this conversation as he walked up to our table. "Great," I thought. "John's questions are way beyond me. And besides that, they're pretty good ones."

"John," Tim said sympathetically, "you've been asking profound questions all week. They've given me new things to think about. But you've also been angry, and I want you to know I understand." Tim put his hand on the doctor's shoulder. "If I had been in your place and had gone through the same pain you've endured these past eight months, I would probably have the same questions and the same arguments. Sometimes you have to get separated by time from severe loss so that you can get in touch with the peace God-Presence tries to give.

"John, give yourself a break. Don't expect so many immediate answers. You're trying to find pat answers to the most difficult questions in life too quickly and too easily. Give your heart some time to heal before you try to come up with conclusions about why this happened to those you loved so deeply.

"I'm sorry I couldn't have done more during this week to help ease the pain. But I'm glad you came — please come back. During the winter, things get quiet here, and perhaps we could have a weekend together to talk and meditate."

Doctor John's eyes filled with tears. He was finally freeing himself to show some emotion. "Thanks, Tim. I don't agree with all you've been saying this week. But I know you do care from the heart. I guess I wanted more answers than I got here, but thanks for listening to me. Thanks for not judging me for rejecting the path you've tried to show me. I know it's going to take me some time to get over this."

Tim looked John straight in the eyes, compassion flooding his face. "Bitterness will never change the facts, but it will change you. Please don't let your feelings and emotions rule all your days. You have too much to offer. You have so much to gain."

As Tim walked away from our table, I wondered to myself what loss the doctor had suffered that was so severe he couldn't face it...or talk to us about it.

My wonderment was short-lived, because all eyes were on me. Bonnie wanted to be last, everyone else had spoken, so that obviously meant it was my turn.

"My story," I said, "is nothing special at all. It's not even that interesting." That didn't seem to matter, so I told them the whole thing, start to finish. My childhood days. College, Connie, my disillusionment with marriage and career, and my disappointment with what I had gained from material things. I told them about the woman at the office, and about my trips to Teotihuacán and Sedona. I told them about *The Celestine Prophecy* and how I came to be at Tocayo.

Then, I tried to explain the previous night — my experience in the meditation room. I told them that I had rejected the notion of Jesus Christ, and rightfully so, I thought, but firmly believed that I had experienced the God-Presence in that quiet room. If the God-Presence — the reality I had sensed firsthand — turned out to be Jesus Christ, I guess I couldn't argue with the fact.

When I finished telling my story, no one spoke for the longest time. Then, finally, Danielle broke the silence. "That's beautiful," she said.

"That's rubbish," countered Doctor John, "but if you think it's going to work for you, I'll just shut up and wait patiently for Bonnie's story."

Mary Beth fiddled with her napkin. "I've never heard before what happens when someone meets the God-Presence, Jeff. I'm glad you told us."

It was Bonnie's turn. At first she seemed reluctant to speak. She stared at her empty plate, and I thought I saw tears welling up in her eyes. When she finally looked up, I could see that it wasn't just my imagination. She was obviously on the edge.

"This has been the most difficult week in my life," she began hesitantly. "No, on second thought, there was one other that was worse."

We offered no words in reply, though most of us had puzzled looks on our faces.

"Coming here, I've had to face something from my past that has been eating at my soul and has been coming between me and the God-Presence. You see," she said, tears streaming down her face, "I know I can't hate another human being and withhold forgiveness and expect the God-Presence to forgive me. I know *The Message* teaches that if I have been forgiven much, I must forgive others...yet it's so hard. I've been fighting this battle most of my life, and especially this week. But that's the reason I came here, so I know I can't leave until I've done what I have to do."

I didn't have a clue as to what Bonnie was talking about, so I had no idea what to say or ask. Fortunately, Danielle must have, because she broke the silence as she gently touched Bonnie's shoulder.

"Bonnie, if you don't want to talk about it, you don't have to. But we're your friends, and we're willing to listen to you and be here for you."

Bonnie wiped her tears with her napkin. As she spoke, I could tell she was struggling with every word. "It was easier to forgive...to put my pain behind me...when I didn't have to confront my past face-to-face. But I deliberately chose to come here, and that left me with no choice."

"Would you mind getting to the point?" asked Doctor John. His tone the entire evening had struck me as far too impatient for a doctor, no matter how much pain he had gone through.

"Give her a break, would you, John?", I said. "This is obviously difficult for her. And if she's not ready to talk, that's okay, too."

"No, it's all right, Jeff," Bonnie said. "I have to get this out."

She spoke so quietly we all had to strain to hear her. "This is not the first time or place I've seen Michael. I was just seven years old when the sound of my mother's screams for help woke me up. I stood at the top of the stairs and watched him plunge a knife into my mother's body over and over."

"Oh, my God!" exclaimed the congresswoman.

We all sat there stunned. Finally, I said, "Go on, Bonnie. We're here for you."

"His trial was an awful time for me," she continued, "I had to testify that he was the man I saw in my house. I was terrified. I knew he'd come back some day and kill me, too.

"The next few years were horrible beyond description. I'd wake up every night with awful nightmares. They were so real...so vivid. I begged my dad to sell our house and move, so that I could get away from all the pain. But he was clinging to the memories of my mom and all the good times that they had in that house. Finally, when I was fifteen, I ran away from home. You know that part of the story — I told you that much at dinner our first night."

We all nodded. Most of us were crying. Our table must have

looked like a collection of world-renowned emotionally impaired people.

"It was Brother Duane who found me on the streets of Hollywood. I was strung out on coke, hitting on the slow-moving cars passing by, hoping to pick up my next john. I just needed a few more bucks to get me through the next day on my next high. He started talking to me, and I knew almost right away he wasn't going to turn into my next trick.

"He told me that there was someone who could show me more love than I had ever experienced before. He said it was the God-Presence — a man named Jesus who became 'God With Us.' I told him he was plain crazy — actually I used more basic language than that — if he believed there was such a thing as a God of love. There was sure no God in my house when my mother was murdered, I told him. There was no such God watching over me when I approached men on the street, not knowing for sure whether or not they were crazy or weird or would beat me. There was no such God when I came down from my high and had to face the day alone and straight.

"And you know what he said? He said I was exactly the kind of person the God-Presence came to love and forgive and change for the better. He told me a story from *The Message* about a woman who was a prostitute. The religious leaders of the time caught her in the act and dragged her half-naked to the marketplace where the God-Presence was teaching. They told him that, according to the ancient laws, she deserved to be stoned. So he said, 'Okay, the one among you who is perfect and has never done anything wrong in your life should be the first to throw a stone.' Not one of them could do it, and they all walked away. Then the God-Presence asked her, 'Where are those who accused you?' She said,

'They've all left.' He said, 'I don't condemn you either. Go now and change your life and turn away from your old ways.'

"Those were the exact words I needed to hear that day. Brother Duane told me many more things about the love of the God-Presence. Then he said that we are to love others and forgive them, and I started crying because I knew there was one person I could never forgive. And that was Michael.

"But I knew I wanted to experience the love and healing he talked about, so I asked the God-Presence to invade my life and make things right. I wanted the fresh start the God-Presence promised.

"From that day forward, I became eager to know what other things the God-Presence had promised that could be mine. And although I loathed the man who murdered my mother, I still found myself caring about him. I thought that if anyone needed to experience the God-Presence, Michael did. And so I asked Brother Duane to visit Michael in prison. You already know the rest of that story."

Mary Beth asked the question that was on all of our minds, I'm sure. "Do you think you're able to do this? Forgive him, I mean?"

"I don't really know," Bonnie answered. "But that's what I came here to do."

I, for one, couldn't believe it. If someone had murdered someone I loved, I don't think I could forgive that person. I couldn't forgive Michael right now, and it wasn't my mother who was senselessly murdered.

"Why do you feel the need to do this?" Mary Beth asked.

Bonnie simply said, "Because the God-Presence commanded me to."

We all knew our conversation was over for the time being. We sat there for a few moments. Some of us cried. Some of us hugged. Some of us closed our eyes and meditated. Some of us, I'm sure, prayed.

Finally, Doctor John rose to his feet and slowly walked out. The others followed, one by one.

Across the table sat Bonnie, still wiping tears from her eyes. She looked up, past me, toward the back of the room. Michael was standing near the exit, talking with Tim.

"This is it," Bonnie said as she placed her napkin on the table and stood up. "This is the perfect time. I have to do this. Pray for me."

"But I don't really know how to pray," I protested.

"Just plead with the God-Presence to give me the strength to forgive, and to mean it like I've never meant anything before."

"I will," I promised.

I didn't even stand up. I sat at the table and watched Bonnie approach Tim and Michael. Tim excused himself and walked away, as if he knew what was about to happen. In retrospect, I'm sure he did know.

Bonnie talked to Michael for what seemed like just a few seconds — less than a minute, for sure. I couldn't hear what she was saying, but I could tell she was crying and he was crying. Then, without warning, they hugged each other in a way I've never seen a man and a woman hug before.

"So that must be what it's all about," I thought, "a brother and a sister and the God-Presence."

Tocayo Legacy

There was nothing Tim or anyone else could say to add to — or take away from — the feelings I had about this night. My experiences at dinner had been so mystical, yet so complete, that I decided I could skip the evening seminar and not miss a thing.

When the chimes rang, I barely looked up from my journal. Let the others gather their thoughts from someone else. I was secure inside my cabin, ready to collect my own.

JOURNAL ENTRY — SATURDAY NIGHT — WHAT A DAY!

And here I thought Bonnie's story could be turned into a TV "Movie of the Week"! That was before I knew even half the story, too.

As it turns out, every story at my table was nearly beyond belief. Except I guess the world is full of hurting people with pasts they would prefer to leave behind them. As "ordinary" as my story is, I too have hurts I want to forget.

If Bonnie illustrated anything to me tonight, it's that we don't have to carry our load around with us for the rest of our lives. The God-Presence seems to be willing and able to take our burdens off our shoulders. I'll bet she feels a lot better after talking to Michael. That had to be the most difficult thing anyone has ever done.

Then again, if the God-Presence really is Jesus Christ, and he really was sent to earth by the celestial God, that must have been a tough thing to do, too. I can't imagine willingly sending a member of my family to a hostile environment to get abused and ridiculed and killed, no matter how noble the cause. It's like sending our sons and daughters to fight a war in a far-off country.

Is that really love, or isn't it?

***

I was so tired that I wasn't even aware of closing my journal and climbing into bed. I don't remember making the transition from awake to asleep.

But the next morning I awoke well before the morning chimes rang, and I headed for the shower while it was still fairly dark outside. I was the only one there, and the water was both hot and wonderfully cleansing.

On the way back to my cabin, I took my time and savored the openness and freshness of Tocayo. I would really miss this place back in the world of Golden Arches and sales quotas and shopping malls. This truly had been a time of in-depth reflection and wonderful insight.

I was filled with mixed emotions. I wanted to get home, to put the experiences I'd had into the everyday language of life.

But I also wrestled with the desire to stay in this kind of a place forever, although a monastic style of living didn't appeal all that much to me. I preferred the challenge of living out this reality of God-Presence in my world. At home. At Josh's hockey games and Amy's soccer matches. At the office, where I battled with my dead-end, tension-filled job.

Hopefully, the important people in my life would somehow understand my experiences at Tocayo — or, at least listen to them and pretend to understand. I was eager to stumble across people who felt the same way about the God-Presence, so that I could further validate my experiences. I knew there had to be others somewhere.

Back at the cabin, I slipped into the clothes I knew would provide the most comfort on the drive back to the airport and the flight home. My flight was at 2:00, but with the time change, I wouldn't show up in my driveway until after 8:00, "Tocayo time." It was going to be a long day.

For some reason, when I go on a trip longer than two or three days, I can never fit everything back into my bags. This time, I seemed to have more leftovers than usual. I was contemplating various solutions to the problem when there was a knock at the door. It was Tim.

"May I come in?" he asked.

"Of course," I answered, as I swung the door wide open.

"Do you have a few minutes? I feel as though we never really finished our conversation yesterday."

"Sure do. That is, if you're in the mood for more of my dumb questions."

"There's no such thing as a 'dumb question,' Jeff. The real trick is not to attach too many dumb answers to all the good ones."

I chuckled. "I know exactly what you mean. I'm beginning to see that I've been asking all the right questions, but I've also been looking in the wrong places for the answers."

"You may think that right now," Tim said, "but the truth is you haven't been looking in the wrong places. Every step of your search has been for a reason, and that reason has been to lead you to the ultimate insight — that the God-Presence is real, caring, loving, forgiving, and can bring order to this chaotic experience we call life. Your favorite book, *The Celestine Prophecy*, wisely teaches that nothing happens to us by chance. But there is a truth beyond that, revealed by *The Message*. And that is that all these things happen to us because *'God knew what he was doing from the very beginning. He decided from the outset to shape the lives of those who love him.'* So you see, the things that happen to you aren't the result of the alignment of the sun, moon, stars, and planets. They're God's doing. I don't know about you, but I'm much more at ease leaving these things in the hands of God than in the hands of my astrological charts."

Tim was right. If the God-Presence really is as he was described in the few pages I'd read in *The Message*, I believed I could become comfortable with his plan for me. So, I asked Tim, "How do I know what to do next? Or tomorrow, or a month from now? How do I know if I'm following his plan?"

"Remember, Jeff, when I explained that no one can become a master overnight? You and I have become life-long learners now. We are both going to make mistakes. And, as I have done so many times, you too are likely going to stray from the individual path the God-Presence has marked out for you. But you can't give up. You can't get discouraged. On those days, you simply have to seek the knowledge of the God-Presence more intently."

"How do I do that? Seek the God-Presence, I mean."

Tim placed his worn, heavily underlined copy of *The Message* in my hands. This," he said, patting the book, "this is how you do it. I want you to have this, Jeff. It's my original copy. I've had it for quite a while now. I'm due for a new one."

"Thank you" was about all I could think of to say to express my gratitude. I really appreciated that Tim would be that willing to part with his book...for me. "But I need to know," I added, "how does this help me in my journey? Is this all there is to it? Frankly, I was hoping for something a great deal more profound."

"Jeff, you remember what happened Friday night in the meditation room? What were you doing when the God-Presence stepped into your very being?"

I thought for a moment. "I was reading *The Message*, and I was talking to the God-Presence as if he were there with me. I think he was, too."

"Exactly!" Tim looked pleased, as he sensed that one of his learners was grasping a profound truth. "You hear the God-Presence speak to you and teach you through reading and meditating on *The Message*. Be willing to take its insights into your mind and soul, and they will impact the way you live. But it's equally important that you communicate back to the God-Presence through prayer. Prayer is not something mechanical; it is conversation. It's far more than form, memorized chants, specific phrases, or liturgical and nostalgic language. It is a sharing, feeling, caring, and enduring communion with the God-Presence. Prayer is the language that binds our relationship with the God-Presence and helps it blossom and deepen in our lives."

This was really coming together for me — really making sense. But I had another question for Tim that couldn't go unanswered.

"What about Connie and the kids? Won't they think I'm nuts?"

"They might."

"Oh, GREAT!"

"But, Jeff, don't treat them like *they're* nuts for not believing the way you do, or for not seeing the Light of the God-Presence just because that Light is visible to you. Everyone who has come to Tocayo this week has had the same opportunity to glimpse the God-Presence. They've attended the same seminars and heard the same stories. But some have not allowed the Light to shine in their lives. You've come home to your father and the celebration in your honor. Others may remain in the distant country for a long time. They may never 'come home.' "

"So you're saying that Connie may never understand?" I asked.

"Possibly. It's not up to me or you or anyone else to say. But please, Jeff, don't judge her. Don't downplay her personal journey. She has to travel that road on her own. You know, I believe it's the judging of well-meaning people that has turned off so many people and caused them to reject the God-Presence — the Christ as he is presented in too many churches. Our task is to love and accept people. Nothing more. Maybe if we could all do that, people would seek the God-Presence before they try all the other things they hope will bring them spiritual enlightenment."

"Well," I added, "you know how I feel about religion. It's that kind of thinking — that kind of attitude — that's kept me away from churches for the past dozen or more years."

"I know, Jeff. That's why it's so exciting to finally understand that the God-Presence has nothing to do with *religion*, and everything to do with *relationship*."

We talked for a few more minutes, about anything and

everything. Then, he got up to leave, and as he walked out the door, he said, "Jeff, I've really enjoyed having you with us this week. You've taught me a lot of things and helped me grow in many ways you'll never know. I hope you'll come back to Tocayo again."

"I will. You can count on it," I called after him as he walked down the narrow path.

After a breakfast filled with animated conversation, I loaded my bags in my rental car and drove down the narrow road toward the main gate. I glanced to my right, and there, seated on lawn chairs, I saw Bonnie and Michael reading something together. I thought it could be *The Message*.

They looked up as I drove by, and as if on cue, they both flashed me the "thumbs up" sign. What a spirit — what a bond — had come over those two!

As I drove through the gates, I said aloud, "People who don't believe in miracles should spend just one week at this place."

A Last Word
to Readers

As you've undoubtedly guessed by now, there is an actual book called *The Message*. It is a modern translation of an ancient Greek text, executed by a scholar by the name of Eugene H. Peterson, who is on the faculty of Regent College in Vancouver, British Columbia.

But to read it and gain anything from it, you will have to suspend a major belief you may have held for years — that sacred writings are meaningless, worthless, irrelevant relics from the past. Because *The Message* is based on an ancient manuscript referred to in our age as "The New Testament," which tells the story of the life and times of one Jesus Christ.

We, the authors, believe that Jesus Christ is the "God-Presence," and that he came to bring light, wisdom, understanding, focus, and energy to our planet, and to gift it to each of us as individuals.

Many modern "enlightened" women and men view the story of Jesus as myth...as an account riddled with errors and omissions...as blown way out of proportion when compared to what may have actually happened. Yet, these same people open their appointment books daily and see a date that is based on a calendar devised around this Jesus' birth and death. Even the dating contained in *The Celestine Prophecy* acknowledges the Gregorian calendar, as it measures history in terms of millennia. Such terms did not even exist at the time the "Manuscript" of *The Celestine Prophecy* was purported to have been written. Those terms came into being because Jesus lived...and lived the pivotal life of all time and eternity.

The same people who doubt the record of the life of Jesus Christ will willingly, without hesitation, accept the writings of Plato and Socrates as true, complete, and accurate. Yet the scientific evidence supporting the biblical records — the sheer number and age of early manuscripts, for example — so outweighs the evidence supporting other historical documents that one could even plausibly wonder if Socrates and Plato ever walked this planet.

However, we did not write this book to provide irrefutable evidence of the existence of the God-Presence — the one we call Jesus Christ. The only evidence that could ever matter to you personally would have to be experiential evidence. You would have to enter into right relationship with God-Presence to know if there is truth in this story. That would have to be the next major step in your journey. As Tim says, "You will not know until you know."

Maybe it's occurred to you that *The Message* would be worthwhile reading. You could bring as much skepticism to this task as you want to. There is nothing wrong with doubt. The only error many of us commit is in not looking for answers in the first place.

You can likely find a paperback copy of *The Message* where you bought this book. Most bookstores have it in the "religion" (we have a strong distaste for that word) section, or they'd be happy to order it for you if it's not in stock.

If you absolutely cannot find it anywhere, you may send $15.00 (plus $3.00 shipping and handling) to the address provided below. Minnesota residents must add 6.5% to 7% sales tax, depending on the locality where they live.

Another book we found very helpful is called *Surprised by Faith*, by Dr. Don Bierle, who holds a Ph.D. in physics. His book is an in-depth analysis of the physical, scientific, and historical evidence related to the Bible and the life of Jesus Christ. This book is difficult to find in bookstores but you may also order it by mail. It is $7.00, plus $3.00 shipping and handling. (Both books may be ordered at the same time for a reduced combined shipping charge of $4.00, but again, Minnesota sales tax must be added.)

The Message says that the path that leads to God-Presence demands your undivided attention. Here are the exact words from page 27 of the paperback edition:

"Don't look for shortcuts to God.
The market is flooded with sure-fire easygoing formulas
for a successful life that can be practiced in your spare time.
Don't fall for that stuff, even though the crowds of people do.
The way to life — and to God! — is vigorous
and requires total attention.
"Be wary of false preachers who smile a lot,
dripping with practiced sincerity.
Chances are they are out to rip you off in some way or other.
Don't be impressed with charisma;
look for character...a genuine leader will never

exploit your emotions or your pocketbook."

Dear readers, we hope we've been leaders guiding you on an important journey. This whole thing isn't about religion. It's about life-changing insights that, when seized by you personally, will impact the rest of your days on this planet.

We hope you'll consider embarking on the journey.

Steve and Ric

P.S. You may write to us with your comments at the same address you can use to order the books we've mentioned if you're unable to find them at the bookstore where you shop. Here it is:

Steve and Ric
THE TOCAYO JOURNEY
P.O. Box 387111
Bloomington, MN 55438-7111